Young Writers
2004 POETRY COMPETITION

ONC
A R

GW00641136

IMAGINATION FOR
A NEW GENERATION

# London & Home Counties
# Vol II

Edited by Steph Park-Pirie

 Young**Writers**

First published in Great Britain in 2004 by:
Young Writers
Remus House
Coltsfoot Drive
Peterborough
PE2 9JX
Telephone: 01733 890066
Website: www.youngwriters.co.uk

SB ISBN 1 84460 615 5

# Foreword

Young Writers was established in 1991 and has been passionately devoted to the promotion of reading and writing in children and young adults ever since. The quest continues today. Young Writers remains as committed to engendering the fostering of burgeoning poetic and literary talent as ever.

This year's Young Writers competition has proven as vibrant and dynamic as ever and we are delighted to present a showcase of the best poetry from across the UK. Each poem has been carefully selected from a wealth of *Once Upon A Rhyme* entries before ultimately being published in this, our twelfth primary school poetry series.

Once again, we have been supremely impressed by the overall high quality of the entries we have received. The imagination, energy and creativity which has gone into each young writer's entry made choosing the best poems a challenging and often difficult but ultimately hugely rewarding task - the general high standard of the work submitted amply vindicating this opportunity to bring their poetry to a larger appreciative audience.

We sincerely hope you are pleased with our final selection and that you will enjoy *Once Upon A Rhyme London & Home Counties Vol II* for many years to come.

Dear Auntie Martine,

have a great Christmas

love from Daniel,

Dec 2004.

# Contents

## Fingringhoe CE Primary School, Colchester

| | |
|---|---|
| Louis Batt  (10) | 13 |
| April Podd  (9) | 14 |
| Henry Maston  (10) | 14 |
| Jack Rodway  (11) | 15 |

## Grange Park Primary School, Grange Park

| | |
|---|---|
| Alex Kypri  (10) | 15 |
| Rhianna Stewart  (10) | 16 |
| Marko Tomic  (10) | 16 |
| Sophie Nicole Yianni  (9) | 17 |
| Gabriella Yianni  (9) | 17 |
| Nicole Hobbs  (10) | 18 |
| Danyel Mustafa  (10) | 18 |
| Sofia Nicolaou  (9) | 19 |
| Eliz Moustafa  (10) | 19 |
| Keelan Shaw  (9) | 20 |
| Anna Soteriou  (9) | 20 |
| Alana Glassey  (10) | 21 |
| Laura Pescow | 22 |
| Tom Simpson  (10) | 22 |
| Pembe Sabri  (10) | 23 |
| Emma Pierce  (10) | 23 |
| Jessica Wood  (9) | 24 |
| Leah Ashcroft-Bravo  (10) | 25 |
| Alice Rafter  (9) | 26 |
| Aliki Georgiou  (10) | 27 |
| Clair Hunnisett  (9) | 28 |
| Dimitri Savva  (10) | 28 |
| Julide Cemal  (10) | 29 |
| Lisa Gransby  (10) | 29 |
| Samara Linton  (10) | 30 |
| Sam Watts  (10) | 30 |
| Hollie Scott  (10) | 31 |
| Anna-Maria Bozovic  (9) | 31 |
| Dion Willoughby  (10) | 32 |
| Charlotte Rhodes  (9) | 32 |
| Lucia Athanasiou  (10) | 33 |
| Odelia Yu  (10) | 33 |
| Amanda Ragnuth  (10) | 34 |
| Abbirhami Ratnarajah  (10) | 34 |

John Holder  (10) 35
Joel Burman  (10) 36
Thomas Clark  (9) 36
Mark Wadsworth  (9) 37
Mark Edwards  (9) 37
Rachel Berkoff  (9) 38
Olivia Ploutarhou  (10) 38
Emily Kourides  (10) 39
Koulla Kazamias  (9) 39
Alicia Santos  (9) 40
Xavier Phillips  (10) 40
Rebecca Gerondaes  (10) 41
Soraya King-Newell  (10) 41
Laura Norton  (10) 42
Maria Arpapi  (10) 42
Annabel Baldwin  (10) 43
Derya Adem  (10) 43
Adam Iqbal  (10) 44
Helena Kouppari  (10) 44
Leo Nagi  (10) 45
Emily Sharp  (9) 45
Kieran Storey  (10) 46
Rory Wood  (9) 46
Thomas Davies-Ahmed  (9) 47

## Hambrough Primary School, Southall

Vanisha Bharadwa  (10) 47
Asha Jimale  (10) 48
Karishma Fatania  (9) 48
Vinojan Vigneswaran  (8) 49
Nada Ahmed  (10) 49
Jehpal Jhita  (10) 50
Parthik Vaghela  (10) 51
Iqra Bhatti  (10) 51
Agalya Rajendran  (9) 52
Amar Cheema  (11) 53
Sophia Shire  (9) 54
Sareena Bassi  (8) 54
Maninder S Matharu  (11) 55
Jatinder Dub  (10) 55
Preet Kaur  (11) 56

## Herbert Morrison School, London

| | |
|---|---|
| Tony Osei-Sarfo  (11) | 78 |
| Christopher Yankson | 78 |
| Lawrence Esan  (11) | 79 |
| Luke Kechane  (11) | 79 |
| Elisabeth Clarke  (12) | 80 |
| Liam Lawrence Stephens  (11) | 80 |
| Michael Asare  (11) | 80 |
| Seniz Kasif  (11) | 81 |
| Lauren Alison Jardine  (11) | 81 |
| Andrew Aikins  (11) | 81 |
| Oluwaseun Adeite  (11) | 82 |
| Jason Kerrane  (11) | 82 |
| Zakee Wilson  (11) | 82 |

## Highwoods Primary School, Colchester

| | |
|---|---|
| Joshua Emm  (8) | 83 |
| Chloe Rutland  (8) | 83 |
| James Taylor  (9) | 84 |
| Liam Mair  (7) | 84 |
| A Year 1 Class Poem | 85 |
| Tiia Barkham  (9) | 86 |
| Lewis Percival  (10) | 86 |
| Tiffany Reeves  (11) | 87 |
| Sam Cullis  (7) | 87 |
| Kat Waring  (10) | 88 |
| Luke Chapman  (8) | 88 |
| Phoebe Connell  (11) | 89 |
| Stuart Clarke  (11) | 90 |
| Jade Bond  (7) | 91 |
| Baha Abdullah  (10) | 91 |
| Zoe Hammond  (10) | 92 |
| Hannah McCarthy  (7) | 92 |
| Tom Wolstenholme  (6) | 92 |
| Ayrand Cruz  (10) | 93 |
| Holly Davies  (10) | 93 |
| Emilie Findlay  (11) | 94 |
| Melissa Warnes  (7) | 94 |
| Lewis Howe  (9) | 94 |
| Lewis Bailey  (10) | 95 |

## Norland Place School, London

| | |
|---|---|
| Lucinda Conder  (8) | 95 |
| Helena Williams  (8) | 96 |
| Eléonore Gomm  (8) | 96 |
| Chloe Smith  (8) | 96 |
| Josie Whitley  (8) | 97 |
| Elsie Hewitt  (8) | 97 |
| Lulu Straker  (8) | 98 |
| Olivia Bryant  (8) | 98 |
| Isa Conroy  (8) | 99 |
| Abigail Hampson  (7) | 99 |
| Olivia Masek  (8) | 100 |
| Eleonore Decaux  (8) | 100 |
| Matilda Moir  (7) | 100 |
| Lujaine Al-Habib  (7) | 101 |
| Zoe Adler  (8) | 101 |
| Amy-Laure Richards  (8) | 102 |
| Jemima Salmon  (7) | 102 |

## Our Lady Of Lourdes RC Primary School, Leigh-On-Sea

| | |
|---|---|
| Shauna McKenny  (11) | 103 |
| Joshua Lewis  (11) | 103 |
| Laura Baillie  (11) | 104 |
| Liam Peoples  (11) | 104 |
| James Seaden  (10) | 105 |
| Laurence Baker  (11) | 105 |
| Karl Sharman  (11) | 106 |
| Aimee Gargan  (8) | 106 |
| Ellen Jeffery  (11) | 107 |
| William Chuck  (11) | 107 |
| Xavier Conner  (11) | 108 |
| Olivia Allen  (10) | 109 |
| Niall Purcell  (11) | 110 |
| Joanna Boosey  (11) | 110 |
| Sam Ridgeway  (11) | 111 |
| Grace Forrai  (7) | 112 |
| Max Robinson  (11) | 112 |
| Cienda Soares  (11) | 113 |
| Chloe Perrotton  (11) | 113 |
| Robert Alani  (11) | 114 |
| Natasha Jaywant  (9) | 114 |

## St John's RC Primary School, Rotherhithe

# The Poems

# Autumn

Autumn is good.
Autumn is chilly, makes my toes all nice and glowy.
The wind goes up and blows in my face.
All my hair goes slowly out of place.
Autumn is good.
Autumn is chilly.
When I close my eyes I picture it fully.

**Sahar Shah  (8)**
Coston Primary School, Greenford


# Friends

Standing there smiling
all the time.
What do I care?
They're always there.
Now they're gone
and my tears are flooding.

**Joe Howse  (9)**
Coston Primary School, Greenford


# My Sister

She is as friendly as a deer.
She is as delicious as a cake.
She looks like a butterfly in the air.
But best of all she is my 13-year-old sister.

**Hannah Treadwell  (10)**
Coston Primary School, Greenford

# Untitled

My dad is so crazy
that he woke lazy.
Now whenever he itches
he puts himself in stitches.

**Kaylah Garvey  (7)**
**Coston Primary School, Greenford**


# What Is Black?

Black is a whale
King of the sea and brave.
Black is feeling scared,
Shivering and frightened.
Black is a zebra's stripes,
Fast and hungry.
Sometimes black is a black, black spot on a ladybird.

**Nyle Malik  (6)**
**Coston Primary School, Greenford**


# What Is . . .

I can do anything, anything at all
I can be a Power Ranger and save the world
I can eat the biggest snails and not be sick
I can be swimmer and not drown.

**Taran Sidhu  (6)**
**Coston Primary School, Greenford**

# The Beach's Secrets

The moonlight glistens down onto
The elegant sandcastles
Children have left behind;
The ebony of the darkness
Stands to form
The golden sand which is now
Filled with tiny footprints
That young children offer
To the beach.
The breeze swims over
To a tall lighthouse,
Newly built,
While the waves of the turquoise
Yet cool sea gather people
To go
For a paddle up and down,
Searching
For the fish that live in the depths
Of the reef.
Mighty dolphins gallop with
The waves waiting for
Humans to come up and kiss
Their silky heads.
The beach
Is a happy place where blunders
Of life are forgiven
For there is no need to be blue.
We are present at the glorious beach.

**Sammy Kaur Sidhu  (9)**
**Coston Primary School, Greenford**

# Rainbow

I sit on my garden path when it rains
waiting to see if a shining rainbow comes.
I say to myself, 'Is there really a pot of shimmering gold at the end
or is it just make-believe?'

**Shannon Baker (10)**
Coston Primary School, Greenford

# What Is Blue?

Blue is a car, shiny and fast,
Blue is a sea in anger,
Blue is a fish, shiny and fast,
Sometimes blue is a blue, blue pen.

**Daine-Louie Baker-Dee (6)**
Coston Primary School, Greenford

# What Is Pink?

Pink is a pig, muddy and rough.
Pink is feeling happy when pink is getting married.
Pink is a toothbrush, brushing and brushing.
Sometimes pink is a pink, pink tongue.

**Kiah Sylvan (6)**
Coston Primary School, Greenford

# What Is Red?

Red is an apple,
Juicy and sweet.
Red is strawberries,
Sugary and sweet.
Sometimes red is a red, red, fire.

**Malachi Buck (5)**
Coston Primary School, Greenford

# Spooky!

One night at my house when the sky was dark and black
I nearly fell asleep in my bed but then I heard a tap.

I saw a shadow on the wall which gave me a little fright.
But then I looked in the distance and saw a little light.

I slowly got out of bed and slowly opened the door.
But when it opened you won't believe what I saw . . .

*Whooooo!*

**Sirtaaj Mattoo  (8)**
**Coston Primary School, Greenford**


# The Castle

It was spooky,
It was freaky,
It was a castle
The size of a giant's parcel.
The garden was fine,
The trees were fifty-nine,
The windows were thick,
The rats had a pick.
The keeper of the castle was a rascal of a spider
Who lived on a rafter
But had hysterical laughter.

**Elias Tourgane  (10)**
**Coston Primary School, Greenford**


# My Naughty Little Sister

My naughty little sister is annoying as can be.
My naughty little sister is the worst I've ever seen.

She's really, really mad but also very bad.
She drives me crazy, up the wall.
She thinks she's Mrs Know-It-All!

**Emily Maguire  (10)**
**Coston Primary School, Greenford**

## Sunset

Sunset is so beautiful
I sit on the bench in the empty park.
I look and think how I would love to touch the beautiful colours.

I think about how much time I've wasted on myself.
I look, I look, I think, I think.
But I cannot help myself.
I want to go help the poor
But I cannot move.
The colours so dazzling, it's amazing how something
So beautiful can stop me from doing something so good.

**Melissa Neocleous (10)**
**Coston Primary School, Greenford**


## What Is . . . ?

Purple is a dress
Nice and beautiful
Purple is feeling happy
Purple is a star
Nice and neat
Sometimes
Purple is a purple, purple
Flower.

**Valantina Yousif (6)**
**Coston Primary School, Greenford**


## About Sisters

Sisters are good.
Sisters are bad.
Sisters are something that you should always love.
Sisters are precious to you.

**Hajera Shaikh (8)**
**Coston Primary School, Greenford**

# Sun And Moon

The sun is yellow.
The sun is hot.
The sun is sparkly.
The sun is round.
The sun is in the sky.
When it comes out it makes me happy!
The moon is white.
The moon is icy cold.
The moon is dull.
The moon is shaped like a banana and sometimes round.
The moon is in the sky.
When it comes out it makes me go to sleep!

**Magdalena Zamojska (8)**
**Coston Primary School, Greenford**


# Sun And Moon

The sun is an opposite to the moon.
The sun is in the sky at daytime.
The sun is yellow-orange with black spots.
The sun is hot.
The sun is big.

The moon is white with black spots.
The moon is cold.
The moon is small.
The moon is in the sky at night.
When these opposites come together
We have perfect harmony just like you and me!

**Charlie Kelleher Gibbons (8)**
**Coston Primary School, Greenford**

# Ghosts Only Come Out At Night

Ghosts are spooky.
Ghosts are white.
Ghosts are scary.
Ghosts are light.
Ghosts are frightening
Quick as lightning.
Ghosts make things go bump in the night
And as the sun rises ghosts disappear with no prize
Only my thought of them in the night.

**Zaynah Rasheed  (8)**
**Coston Primary School, Greenford**


# What Is Yellow?

Yellow is a daffodil
Long and lovely
Yellow is feeling happy
Yellow is a lion
King and cross
Sometimes yellow is a yellow, yellow sun.

**Roslyn Mchomvu  (5)**
**Coston Primary School, Greenford**


# What Is Pink?

Pink is a pig
Light and heavy.
Pink is feeling happy
With a smile.
Pink is a Barbie doll
Beautiful and lovely.
Sometimes
Pink is a pink, pink
Ice cream.

**Priya Patel  (6)**
**Coston Primary School, Greenford**

# I Can Do Anything

I can be Batman and fight how baddies would.
I can keep a dinosaur for a pet.
I can make a tree house.
I can ride a leopard.
I can run like a leopard.
I can climb the tallest house.
I can do anything, anything at all.

**Marcin Zamojski (6)**
Coston Primary School, Greenford


# What Is Blue?

Blue is a mountain, rocky and cold.
Blue is feeling bright in the sky.
Blue is a rainy day, wet and splashy.
Sometimes blue is a blue, blue sea.

**Salman Shaikh (6)**
Coston Primary School, Greenford


# What Is Red?

Red is an apple
Sweet and yummy.
Red is feeling brave
With all my might.
Red is a ladybird
Smooth and shiny.
Sometimes red is a red, red car.

**Ravi Nandha (6)**
Coston Primary School, Greenford

# What Is Brown?

Brown is a bear, soft and furry.
Brown is feeling angry, kicking a ball.
Brown is a coconut, hard and yummy.
Sometimes brown is a brown, brown eye.

**Michael Neocleous (6)**
**Coston Primary School, Greenford**


# I Can Do Anything

I can do anything, anything at all.
I can be a butterfly and fly all over the world.
I can be a princess and live in a castle.
I can mix potions all day.
I can do anything, anything at all.

**Imaan Jan (6)**
**Coston Primary School, Greenford**


# Untitled

Kim the rainbow dog
Found a round log
Inside was a clock
That went tick-tock.

**Aaminah Kahn (7)**
**Coston Primary School, Greenford**


# My Friend Sam

My friend Sam
Heard a loud bam!
It blew out her ear
And then she couldn't hear!

**Rhiannon Dempsey (8)**
**Coston Primary School, Greenford**

# Dazzling Stars In The Night-Time Sky

When it is night-time I look out my window
and into the night-time sky
which is always filled with dazzling white stars
that brighten the world and brighten my heart.
Every star is a different symbol of joy and peace and love.

**Dan James Robertshaw  (10)**
**Coston Primary School, Greenford**


# What Is Pink?

Pink is a dress
Beautiful and nice.
Pink is feeling warm and shy.
Pink is a flower
Smelly and sweet.
Sometimes
Pink is a pink, pink
Pig.

**Caitlin Cross  (6)**
**Coston Primary School, Greenford**


# Spooky Poem!

One night I had a fright
And the room looked
Like a spooky night.

The house looked like a dark place
With all the ghosts having a race
In a funny night.
In this place it felt tight on the other side of my bed.

**Natalie Dash**
**Coston Primary School, Greenford**

# What Is Green?

Green is a frog
Silly and jumpy.
Green is feeling sick
With slime straight out.
Green is a flower
Nice and smelly.
Sometimes
Green is a green, green
Tree.

**Sulaymaan Dar  (6)**
**Coston Primary School, Greenford**


# I Can Do Anything

I can do anything, anything at all.
I can be Batman.
I can keep a Batman car.
I can climb a tall building.
I can swim across the river.
I can fly to the moon.
I can do anything, anything at all.

**Nishaan Kailarajan  (6)**
**Coston Primary School, Greenford**


# Shopping

I'm a shopoholic because I like to shop
I shop all day and I shop 'til I drop
I shop and shop 'til there's nothing in stock
I love to shop and there's no one to stop!

**Nicola Shar & Sophia Rasheed  (10)**
**Coston Primary School, Greenford**

# Girls, Boys And Toys

Shaqueil the Black
Had a big sack
And he handed out toys
To the girls and boys.

**Scott McDermott (8)**
**Coston Primary School, Greenford**

# The Angry Sea

The angry sea
A giant monster
Hammering on the bottom
Of the cliffs.

The sea spurts up
I hear the storm
As it shouts out
A huge roar.

Some of the cliff
Goes crashing down.
The water all
Showers upon the land.

The sea turns into
A jug that spills
Among all the land.

Cracks travel up
One side of a cliff,
The sea smashes
On the cliff's weak point.

You hear the crack
Then the cliff tumbles down.
All the water spurts up
And a crash of thunder strikes.

**Louis Batt (10)**
**Fingringhoe CE Primary School, Colchester**

# The Angry Sea

Pounding and scolding against the cliff ahead
Like a roaring lion
The cliff crumbles as it erodes
The house on top plunges into the frosting sea
Swallowed by the sea below
The wind blows fiercely in the raging sky
The sea is beating against the subsiding cliff
The weather dies down
Finally the cliff gives way and comes crashing in
Now all that's left is a bay.

**April Podd  (9)**
**Fingringhoe CE Primary School, Colchester**


# Angry Sea

Angry sea hammering at the coastline,
Fierce waves shattering and beating at the soft cliffs,
Like a Tyrannosaurus-rex,
When is it going to stop?

It shatters at the crumbly cliffs,
It breaks into a million pieces that fall into the angry, rough sea,
In the night the sea's plain blue,
But in the morning it's white as a piece of paper
And as foamy as bubble bath.

**Henry Maston  (10)**
**Fingringhoe CE Primary School, Colchester**

# The Angry Sea

The sea battering against the cliffs
Pieces of the cliff scatter down to the bottom of the sea,
The sea spraying in the air like a tornado
Rain pelting down from the dark, angry sky.

The thunder roaring like a lion
Lightning flashing like a powerful torch running out of batteries,
Another huge wave crashing back down to the sea,
Then slowly the sea dies down and the sun comes out.

**Jack Rodway  (11)**
**Fingringhoe CE Primary School, Colchester**


# Open The Door

The door
The door
Open the door to see inside it
I see the sky moving as the door opens
I see the world with magic around it
With spells sprinkling around.

The door
The door
The world moving around
Open the door to see a brand new world.

The door
The door
I open the door
I see a brand new life.

**Alex Kypri  (10)**
**Grange Park Primary School, Grange Park**

# My Brother

My brother is horrid
My brother is mean
He loves to fight like a machine
He is always around
Playing in the ground
Digging stuff up that shouldn't be found
My brother is tough
He always plays rough
He doesn't get told off enough
He gets in a temper
He screams and shouts
And creates havoc all about
I love my brother when he is good
So when he's in a really bad mood
I talk to him quietly.
'Hey, want to play?'
Then he's friendly for the rest of the day.

**Rhianna Stewart  (10)**
**Grange Park Primary School, Grange Park**


# Freedom

Freedom is to be yourself,
Freedom is your life,
Freedom is to be free,
Freedom is to do what you want,
Freedom is not to be a slave,
Freedom is everything you wish for
And freedom is the only thing I would die for.

**Marko Tomic  (10)**
**Grange Park Primary School, Grange Park**

# Cats And Dogs

Cats and dogs are always fighting
They chase all night
Scratching and biting.

They disappear along the street
The cat and dog
Snapping at feet.

They create lots of noise in people's faces
Then stroll off proudly
To play races.

At the end of the day I call my pets in
While the cat sleeps
The dog barks out, 'I win.'

**Sophie Nicole Yianni  (9)**
**Grange Park Primary School, Grange Park**


# Brother

My brother is the best boy in the world
When he runs he gets in a twirl.

I love him a lot, he's got a great touch
But sometimes he annoys me very much.

He laughs every day in his own special way
And he really likes to happily play.

My brother is sweet, but can be sly and sneaky
He has rosy cheeks and is ever so clever.
He's the cutest boy and I'll love him *forever!*

**Gabriella Yianni  (9)**
**Grange Park Primary School, Grange Park**

# The Island Of Dreams

Mexico, Mexico
The island of dreams, the sun shone hot as it beamed on me.
Mexico, Mexico
I wish I was there.

The beach, the beach
Was lovely with the sun but the island of dreams, it has gone.
Mexico, Mexico
The beach has gone.

Mexico, Mexico
The sea was warm and as clear as diamonds.
Island of dreams, island of dreams
Where have you gone?

**Nicole Hobbs (10)**
**Grange Park Primary School, Grange Park**


# Freedom

Freedom is privacy,
To be who you are,
Freedom's not loneliness,
Just staring at a star.

Freedom is happiness,
To see the world your way,
Freedom's not cruelty,
Just be happy all day.

Freedom is to be free,
Do what you feel is right,
Freedom's not to feel sorrow,
All day and all night.

Freedom.

**Danyel Mustafa (10)**
**Grange Park Primary School, Grange Park**

# Brothers

My brothers are quite naughty,
And sometimes are unkind,
They break my things and hide them,
And I really, really mind.

I tell them not to do this,
That they're being quite unfair,
But they just laugh and giggle
Because they do not care.

My mum says they'll outgrow this,
That they're only being boys,
She tells them if they carry on,
That she will hide *their* toys!

But in the end I must admit,
I really am the same,
I break their toys and hide them,
And I never get the blame!

**Sofia Nicolaou  (9)**
**Grange Park Primary School, Grange Park**


# My Sister

My sister is a pain,
She drives me insane,
Sometimes she is sweet,
My parents think she's a treat,
She always gets her own way,
Does she get told off? No way!
I stamp upstairs,
Because no one cares,
I would not drive my mum wild,
If I was an only child!

**Eliz Moustafa  (10)**
**Grange Park Primary School, Grange Park**

## Countries

It's burning sun lights the day
And rugby's what they play
At the beach the sand is scorching
But in the sea it's not so warming.

What country am I?

Its chilling snow
Will freeze anyone's toe
It's freezing ice
Is too cold for mice.

What country am I?

The home of the Olympics
Where men work with pickets
They have old gifts
And they have old myths.

What country am I?

**Keelan Shaw (9)**
**Grange Park Primary School, Grange Park**


## A Christmas Poem

The world outside is icy and cold,
The land is white with snow.

Oh, Christmas fairy, bless our homes,
And set our hearts aglow.

Christmas fairy, light our lives,
With happiness and cheer.

Warm our hearts, set cares aside,
At this wondrous time of year.

**Anna Soteriou (9)**
**Grange Park Primary School, Grange Park**

# The Door

*(Inspired by 'The Door' by Miroslav Holub)*

Go and open the door
Maybe outside there's:
A flower, a bush
A park
Or a field full of glitter.

Go and open the door
Maybe outside there's:
A cloudy, shadowy mist
A hand reaching for you
Or a nail
Or an image
Of an image.

Go and open the door
If there's a mess
It will clear.

Go and open the door
Even if there's only
The air awaiting you,
Even if there's only
The rain pouring in,
Even if
    Nothing
        Is there
Go and open the door.

At least
There'll be
Your garden.

**Alana Glassey (10)**
**Grange Park Primary School, Grange Park**

# In The Clouds I Saw . . .

In the clouds I saw
a biting, fighting lamb and a pink pig eating Sam!

In the clouds I saw
a cat driving a truck and a horseshoe bringing luck!

In the clouds I saw
Metin playing football and Talia looking cool!

In the clouds I saw
Kelly doing her hair and Pembe climbing the stairs!

In the clouds I saw
Keelan jumping around and Stelio not making a sound!

In the clouds I saw
Coris talking a lot and Ali lying in a cot!

In the clouds I saw
Josh making jokes and Eve drinking Coke!

In the clouds I saw
Emma having a swim and Matthew looking dim!

In the clouds I saw
Nicola throwing rocks and Julide picking a lock!

Now the clouds are starting to bend
this poem has to come to an end!

**Laura Pescow**
**Grange Park Primary School, Grange Park**


# My Family

Dad does too much building,
My sister does too much singing,
Mum does too much cleaning,
George does too much telling,
Alfie does too much crying,
I don't do enough reading!

**Tom Simpson  (10)**
**Grange Park Primary School, Grange Park**

# Grandma's Milkshakes

Grandma's milkshakes are the best
Especially her special recipe
They're better than all the rest.

Because they are creamy
Chocolaty they have a bit
Of everything in.
They spin and swirl and dance and twirl.

Grandma's milkshakes are the best
Especially her special recipe
They're better than all the rest.

**Pembe Sabri  (10)**
**Grange Park Primary School, Grange Park**


# Sweet Shop

I'm off down the sweet shop
I've got my 50p
Mum said that's all I could have
For after my tea
What shall it be?
Shall it be a jelly curl?
Or some bubblogum?
Or maybe even a lemon drop?
Is that the sweet for me?

Decisions, decisions
What shall it be?
What shall I choose?
What's for me?
I think it's got to be a sherbet dip
I think that's the one for me!

**Emma Pierce  (10)**
**Grange Park Primary School, Grange Park**

# The Lady Of The Lake

As the sun sets behind high peak mountains,
Shimmers on the trees and fountains,
Awoke the Lady of the Lake,
Who slept through day, at night would wake.

Her hair is elegant streaks of gold,
So the people would have told,
Her face is an entrancing pearly-white,
Her lips are red, such a magnificent sight.

When she walks across the earthly ground,
She makes no patter, she makes no sound,
All the animals would walk by her side,
As she would sparkle, as she would glide.

One day a man called Sir Henry Drake,
Took the Lady of the Lake,
And made her be his beautiful queen,
And be locked in a tower never to be seen.

Soon the Lady got seriously ill,
Nothing could help her, no medicine or pill,
They got magicians from north, east, south and west,
But none could help, not even the best.

As she lay on her woven, silk bed,
She called her maid and then she said,
'My death has come so very near,
So take me to the place that is so dear.'

So the maid took the Lady of the Lake,
To where she slept through day, at night would wake,
And the Lady then fell and peacefully died,
A smile on her face while the people mourned and cried.

**Jessica Wood  (9)**
**Grange Park Primary School, Grange Park**

# Weather

Snow snowy
A chilly breeze
Snow snowy
You're gonna freeze.

Sun sunny
Baking hot
Sun sunny
Like sizzling pot.

Rain rainy
A cold shower
Rainy, rainy
It's got some power.

Cloud cloudy
Covering the sky
Cloud cloudy
Like when it's shy.

Wind windy
Whooshing away
Wind windy
Come another day.

Thunder, thundery
Like hand drums
Thunder thundery
Like cross mums.

*Boom! Crash!*

**Leah Ashcroft-Bravo (10)**
**Grange Park Primary School, Grange Park**

# The Book Of The Dead

One day I went to the library,
The day was cold and wet.
I found a book with a gold spine and leather cover,
It was called 'The Book Of The Dead'.

The book sucked me inside,
I was swirling all around.
So fast that I felt like I was blind,
Then *thump* - I hit the ground.

What was this place - this unknown world?
The sky was in darkness for the moon did not show.
A fire-breathing dragon flew above my head,
With enormous wings that seemed to glow.

Then I jumped in fright,
Dead bodies were on the floor.
Their skins were cold and paralysed,
I was scared, I could say no more.

Now I panicked, now I screamed,
I wished that I could get away.
To my relief that book took me back,
Back to my normal world of play.

Good, it's just me,
Alice of thirteen,
Hoping I've not been away for too long!
But where is that book?
It's vanished!
Gone!
That book that took me away . . .
That book that I will never look at again.

**Alice Rafter (9)**
**Grange Park Primary School, Grange Park**

# Teachers

Teacher being horrible and beastly,
Teacher being scared of the sun,
Teacher being a greedy pig,
Teacher being in love.

Teacher being chubby,
Teacher being crazy,
Teacher being out of school,
Teacher being a footballer.

Teacher being messy,
Teacher having a bad hair day,
Teacher being naughty and mischievous,
Teacher being a cry baby.

Teacher being a baby,
Teacher can't speak,
Teacher being dumb,
Teacher being pregnant.

Teacher being a mad painter,
Teacher being particularly not perfect,
Teacher being phone crazy,
Teacher being an idiot to Mr Smith.

Teacher going swimming,
Teacher being on payback time,
Teacher being a dog,
Teacher being a goldfish.

Teacher being a pop star,
Teacher being a rock star,
Teacher being on TV,
Teacher being a pencil.

Teacher getting sacked,
Teacher getting married.

**Aliki Georgiou (10)**
**Grange Park Primary School, Grange Park**

# Black Magic

I walk down the dusty path,
Not knowing what to do,
Then it's lying there in front of me,
Not knowing if it is old or new.

It seems to be a book,
A book like no other,
I read the first word,
It says 'mother'.

What type of book is it?
Magic, non-fiction or story?
It must be a magic book,
Wait, there's a voodoo doll called Tory.

It is outside an old mill,
We call it the haunted house,
I start to walk inside the house,
Everything quiet as a mouse.

*Boom!* That's what I heard,
Then I start to scream,
I looked round the corner of the door,
It was a very bright beam.

It took my head from behind the door,
It was a big creep,
Suddenly I woke up,
Phew, it's just a deep sleep.

**Clair Hunnisett  (9)**
**Grange Park Primary School, Grange Park**


# Man From France

There was an old man from France,
He had an elaborate lance,
In less than an hour,
His lance was a flower,
He sniffed it and did a small dance!

**Dimitri Savva  (10)**
**Grange Park Primary School, Grange Park**

# I'm Really Ill

Mum, Mum, I'm really ill,
I have a fever and a chill,
I'm turning green, I'm turning blue,
I have a cold and a flu,
I have the sweats, I have the shakes,
I'm coming down with a bellyache,
My knees are weak, my vision's bad,
My throat is sore, I'm really sad,
And did I mention you won't be glad?
I sprained an ankle, fractured a toe,
The school nurse even said so,
So, Mum, can I stay at home today?
I'll read, paint, I'll even pray.

**Julide Cemal  (10)**
**Grange Park Primary School, Grange Park**


# I Hate My Hairdresser!

I hate my hairdresser, she is boring,
I hope my mum doesn't wake up from her snoring,
She cut my eyebrows right to the rim,
I fainted and fell in the large dustbin.

I hate my hairdresser, she is a bully,
She cut my hair off almost fully,
I think I hear my mum, she is coming downstairs,
She is eating two large, juicy pears.

I hate my hairdresser, she is bad,
I hear the doorbell ring, it is my dad,
He took me to my enemy hairdresser,
And said, 'It looks much better!'

**Lisa Gransby  (10)**
**Grange Park Primary School, Grange Park**

# Island In The Sun

Jamaica, Jamaica, the island in the sun,
It is more precious to me than to anyone.

It is where I was born and lived for 7 years,
When I moved to England I was filled with tears.

I miss my friends, my school and the house of mine,
The beaches, the palm trees and mostly the sunshine.

The plants there are green and forever in bloom,
There are birds to feed and horses to groom.

It is always summer and never cold,
Everyone is welcome, young and old.

Jamaica, Jamaica, the island in the sun,
It is more precious to me than to anyone.

**Samara Linton (10)**
**Grange Park Primary School, Grange Park**


# Snapper

I had a turtle named Snapper
*He died, he died.*
Mum said he ran away
*She lied, she lied.*
Snapper was my only friend
But when he died
I tried to send
A letter to my mum to say
Why did she lie to me that day?
*Then she died, she died.*
Dad said she was sleeping,
*He lied, he lied.*
First I was glad
But now I am so very sad.

**Sam Watts (10)**
**Grange Park Primary School, Grange Park**

# Secret

Tell me your secret,
I'll keep my mouth shut tight,
I won't let it out, not even with a fight.

Tell me your secret,
I won't speak a word,
I won't tell anyone, not even a bird.

Tell me your secret,
It won't slip my mouth,
I'll lock it up safely under the ground.

Tell me your secret,
I swear on my life,
If I let it out I'll kill myself with a knife.

Tell me your secret,
I promise I won't laugh,
If I let myself giggle I'll make myself starve.

Tell me your secret,
Please, please, *please,*
If you won't tell me, I'll beg on my knees.

**Hollie Scott  (10)**
**Grange Park Primary School, Grange Park**


# Time!

If all times were good
And nothing was bad
My life would be easier
Nothing would be sad.

Make your life better
By being yourself
Or helping the world
Keep in good health.

**Anna-Maria Bozovic  (9)**
**Grange Park Primary School, Grange Park**

# Clouds

In the clouds I saw a T-rex eating a triceratops
I saw a person milking a cow
A saw a heart shape in the clouds
And an old man snoring in his rocking chair
And a snowman dressing in the clouds
There was an elephant on a car
A rhino pushing a lorry
I saw an egg crack
I saw a boy doing a back flip on his bike.

**Dion Willoughby (10)**
Grange Park Primary School, Grange Park

# Please Can I Open It?

What could it be?
It looks rather long
It could be those shoes
But then I could be wrong.

What could it be?
It feels rather light
Oh I wish I could open it
But it's wrapped up too tight.

What could it be?
Does it make a sound?
I shake it really forcefully
Is it a clown?

I ripped open the paper
To see what it was
Then I found out.
It was a pair of odd socks.

**Charlotte Rhodes (9)**
Grange Park Primary School, Grange Park

# Cinderella

Poor Cinderella found it tough,
Scrubbing stains she'd had enough.

All her sadness gathered up
And poor Cinderella was told, 'Shut up.'

Her three horrid stepsisters
Where so ugly they had blisters.

How many tempers they had had,
Everyone around them would go mad.

Their dream was a magic ball,
But all they got was a prince and a hall.

Cinderella was all alone,
With no one there to moan and groan.

Then along came the magic blond,
Who began to wave her wand.

With a flash of bright light,
Everything was put right.

Cinderella was put on a throne,
While her sisters could only groan.

**Lucia Athanasiou (10)**
**Grange Park Primary School, Grange Park**


# The Seaside!

I looked on the guide to find the seaside,
Then we looked here and there to find a deckchair,
Then my mum lay on it and she loved every bit,
Then my brother and me swam in the sea,
I made a castle out of sand with my salty hands,
Then the sun went down and I began to frown,
Then it was time to go and we all said, 'Oh no!'

**Odelia Yu (10)**
**Grange Park Primary School, Grange Park**

# Secret

Tell me your secret,
I won't tell anybody
I'll guard it with all my strength.

Tell me your secret,
Tell me please, oh please!
I will put it in a bottle and sail it off to sea.

Tell me your secret
And you will thank me for this
I'll keep it in my heart safe and sound.

Tell me your secret
Oh please, won't you tell me?
I will keep it forever and will never reveal it.

Tell me your secret
Why not me?
I'll keep it shut in my mind.

**Amanda Ragnuth (10)**
**Grange Park Primary School, Grange Park**


# Thanks

Thanks for the food
That someone may eat.

Thanks for water
That we can drink.

Thanks for the sun
That keeps us alive.

Thanks for the trees
That give us oxygen.

Thanks!

**Abbirhami Ratnarajah (10)**
**Grange Park Primary School, Grange Park**

# The Door

Go and open the door
Maybe outside there's
A pond or the sea,
A beach or a magical garden.

Go and open the door
Maybe outside there's
A wolf foraging
Maybe you'll see a riot
Or a nose
Or the president
Of the White House.

Go and open the door
If there's a tidal wave
It will clear.

Go and open the door
Even if there's only
The light shining
Even if there's only
The cold wind
Even if
    Nothing
        Is there.

Go and opon the door
At least
There'll be
Your homework.

**John Holder  (10)**
**Grange Park Primary School, Grange Park**

# The Dark And Lonely Forest

Darker and darker the forest tends to grow,
Deeper my heart demands me to go!

My destiny lies beyond these green trees,
I want to be free, just help me, oh please!

The eerie noises make me jump out of my skin,
For some reason the trees have an evil grin!

Their outstretched branches try to take me back to the start,
'No way, that's not happening!' shouts me and my heart!

This forest is so creepy and so scary for me,
But then I hear a beautiful voice saying,
'Come in from the garden it's time for your tea!'

**Joel Burman  (10)**
**Grange Park Primary School, Grange Park**


# Freedom

There should be no slaves
In this world that we live,
We should not be ruled
But do as we please.

We should be free
To do as we want,
To play all around
And have some great fun.

We were born as free
As the birds in the sky,
To speak aloud our minds
'Til the day we die.

**Thomas Clark  (9)**
**Grange Park Primary School, Grange Park**

# Cars

Engines roaring, tyres screeching
Wheels skidding, brakes screaming
Wheels turning, shining smoothly
Indicators clicking when you're
Turning on the highway.

Formula 1 racing down the track
Braking at the pit stop
And screeching at the cracks
Stopping at the petrol station
And learning to have patience.

Speeding down the motorway
Trying to get home
When a man in a Ferrari
Comes speeding past
In a lane all of his own.

A woman in a Lamborghini
Came speeding down the motorway
And didn't even see me
When I had the indicators on
You'd think she was a loony.

**Mark Wadsworth (9)**
**Grange Park Primary School, Grange Park**


# The Moon

It is like a torch and glows all night,
It orbits the Earth every day
And reflects light.
The only way kids can reach it
Is by flying a kite,
Living on the moon should be the life.

**Mark Edwards (9)**
**Grange Park Primary School, Grange Park**

# Noises

Clickity-clack goes the train on the track,
Tickity-tock goes the grandpa clock.

'Bang, bang,' shouts Jane talking slang,
Crash, crash go burglars taking cash.

Crunch, crunch goes the apple in my lunch,
Ding-dong goes the organ's song.

Clickity-clack,
Tickity-tock,
Bang, bang,
Crash, crash,
Crunch, crunch,
Ding-dong,
This is my poem song!

**Rachel Berkoff (9)**
**Grange Park Primary School, Grange Park**


# Swing

Swing, swing in the air,
Over trees as people stare,
Up and down, your bum so numb,
Don't look round or you'll scream, 'Mum!'

Up so high in the sky,
See the birds flying by,
Look at the blossom on the trees,
Then you'll hear the buzzing of the bees!

See the flowers on the grass,
Look at the butterfly fluttering past,
Swing, swing in the air,
Over trees as people stare.

**Olivia Ploutarhou (10)**
**Grange Park Primary School, Grange Park**

# Super Alliouper!

Super Alliouper jumping shoes,
Wear them and jump as high as you choose,
Jump to the moon, jump to the stars,
Go to Venus or go to Mars.

Super Alliouper flying cape,
The fabulous cape that will help you escape,
Fly above the mountains, fly above the oceans,
This amazing cape will raise your emotions.

Super Alliouper humorous hat,
Tell comical jokes which aren't flat,
You will really be popular in a flash,
People will follow you like you've got the cash.

Super Alliouper!

**Emily Kourides  (10)**
**Grange Park Primary School, Grange Park**


# Victorian Children

Victorian children, smelly and not clean
Some are happy, some are mean.

Victorian children dressed in rags
All their belongings in paper bags.

Boys were more important
Than all the girls back then
Along Victorian reformers came
Now we are treated all the same.

**Koulla Kazamias  (9)**
**Grange Park Primary School, Grange Park**

# My Cat

My cat is lazy, she sits around all day,
She can't find her way home, she goes the wrong way.
When I put her food down, she makes a funny sound,
My mum wants her to put on some pounds.

She poops on my bed, where I rest my head,
She doesn't eat her food, but she does eat bread.
Her name is Rosietta, my mum chose the name,
She is so boring, she doesn't want to play games.

Now you know all about my cat,
Yes, you know that she is not fat.
She is cute and cuddly and ginger too,
Ahh, Rosietta, I do love you!

**Alicia Santos (9)**
**Grange Park Primary School, Grange Park**


# Winter

Winter can be such a joy
And you can have lots of fun
With snowballs flying through the air
Until the day is done.

Sure playing in the sun is fun
But winter is much better
You can have loads of snowball fights
And there is no change of weather.

Some people think winter is bad
But I have to disagree
It may make them feel very sad
But it makes me feel quite happy.

**Xavier Phillips (10)**
**Grange Park Primary School, Grange Park**

# Cats

Cats are loving when you're down
Cats are playful when you are around.
They're lovable, beautiful, cuddly too
They're fluffy and caring and they love you!

*Cats!*

**Rebecca Gerondaes (10)**
**Grange Park Primary School, Grange Park**


# Dream Sweets

Bubbly chocolate,
Fizzy sweets,
Squishy marshmallows,
What a treat.

Dangling laces,
Sticky gum,
Sour straws,
In my tum.

Flying saucers,
Sherbet dips,
Make me want,
To lick my lips

Curly Whirlies,
Chockie bars,
Especially Milky Ways
And Mars.

So many lovely, yummy, yum yums,
But don't forget your teeth and gums,
Eat your sweeties but all the while,
Consider your beautiful, dazzling smile.

**Soraya King-Newell (10)**
**Grange Park Primary School, Grange Park**

# When My Teacher Lost His Pants!

Just another school day,
One dull Monday morning,
Handing in our homework,
It was so boring.

Until my teacher
Came through the door
And then his trousers
Dropped to the floor.

We all started screaming
And began to cheer,
When our TA looked round,
She began to jeer.

He didn't really notice,
He didn't seem to care,
Until he looked down
And saw his underwear!

**Laura Norton (10)**
**Grange Park Primary School, Grange Park**


# My Sister

My sister is so boring,
She keeps on snoring
And when she goes to bed at night
She really is a sorry sight!

My sister says appalling jokes
That make me want to cringe
And when I tell her to shut up
She has a right old whinge!

**Maria Arpapi (10)**
**Grange Park Primary School, Grange Park**

# Chucki The Genius

Chucki the genius is an amazing bird,
I tell you once and once again he's no ordinary nerd!
He knows 26 letters of the alphabet and numbers to eternity
And guess who taught him all of this? Nobody but me!
I taught him javelin and triple jump, athletics and plenty more.
I showed him how to be real fierce,
Like a lion with a huge, loud roar!
I trained him to be soooo so posh, with manners and all that lot.
I advised him of the three w's, when, why and what!
So, Chucki the genius is an amazing talking bird.
I tell you once and once again he's no ordinary nerd!

**Annabel Baldwin (10)**
**Grange Park Primary School, Grange Park**


# For Sale

My sister is a clumsy brute,
She staggers down the stairs.
Coming to get her breakfast,
Which is always eggs and pears!

She gulps it down with olive oil,
And a mug of coffee too.
Then she climbs the stairs again,
And doesn't flush the loo!

She stomps her dirty feet around,
Shaking the slippery, quaky ground.
But right now she's in a good mood,
Wait till you see her be really rude!

In exchange for this I would like
A sister who can ride a bike
Or maybe one that is so cool
She could make me rule the school!

**Derya Adem (10)**
**Grange Park Primary School, Grange Park**

# Fast Cars

Driving down the alleyway,
Making all the people sway.
Becoming furious, going fast,
Not able to stop the terrible blast.

Skidding round the sharp corner,
Burning wheels, getting warmer.
Axle can't stop spinning,
Until the driver stars winning.

Now crossing the chequered flag,
Screeching to a stop with a drag.
Jumps out onto the plain,
Then fires away with champagne!

**Adam Iqbal  (10)**
**Grange Park Primary School, Grange Park**


# My Cat

My cat, what does he do all night
When we all go to bed?
Does he get in a fight?
No, not my little Ted.
It's a mystery
But what does he do all night?
It's no mystery,
He simply sleeps all night.

**Helena Kouppari  (10)**
**Grange Park Primary School, Grange Park**

# My Pet

I have a pet
His name is Spiked
He looks weird
And will give you a fright.

He has red hair
And has a horn
He is extremely tall
And his favourite food is corn.

He lives in a sea
And can shout really loud
I can hear him from miles
And he can jump over a cloud.

He is my pet
And I love him a lot
He is my best friend
But sometimes he gets tied in a knot.

*He is Spiked!*

**Leo Nagi  (10)**
**Grange Park Primary School, Grange Park**


# Dolphins

Dolphins are playful,
Friendly when you're around,
Loving and caring when you're down.

Crystal-blue in the sun,
They want to have so much fun,
Beautiful, lovely, they can be,
Sweet and smooth, you will see.

**Emily Sharp  (9)**
**Grange Park Primary School, Grange Park**

# Greens

Greens are so healthy,
Always go well with rice.
Dipped in curry sauce,
Makes you strong and nice.

Greens make you fast,
They make you see in the dark.
They make your muscles grow,
And swim as fast as a shark.

**Kieran Storey  (10)**
**Grange Park Primary School, Grange Park**


# Potions

Eye of newt, cats' tails
In goes a boot and snails,
Lovely sound of screaming
When the boy goes in steaming.

Then Matilda sticks in her rose,
Nasty old toad goes in for those,
Teeth from Dracula teeming with blood,
Donated for a bite of fudge.

But nobody else wants to taste
The wonderful, magical paste.
They're all eating vegetable soup
So I decided to have a snoop.

I found the magical recipe
With great reading intensity
I found out what was missing.
I forgot the snake tongue hissing.

**Rory Wood  (9)**
**Grange Park Primary School, Grange Park**

# My Food

My mummy calls me down to eat
Oh, it's that time again
I hope she's not cooked veg and meat
Last time it was a strain!

When she calls me down again
I feel my stomach churn
I approach the dinner table
The point of no return!

**Thomas Davies-Ahmed  (9)**
**Grange Park Primary School, Grange Park**


# Westbrook Sunset

*(Tongaat - South Africa)*

As I stood on
the yellow sands
of Westbrook,
the deep, blue sea
washed over my
feet.
I felt a sudden
tingle.
The sun was shining
like glitter.
The sun slowly vanished
into the clouds.
I smelled the richness
of the braai.
The orange-coloured sun
finally set in the
sky.

**Vanisha Bharadwa  (10)**
**Hambrough Primary School, Southall**

# Freedom And Justice

Injustice will take over
the world because of colour.

In the day of apartheid
great men walked the earth
fighting for equal rights
we stood together on the mountaintop
and shouted, 'Freedom and justice!'

All the great leaders
Luther, Kennedy, Ghandi, Mandela.

I see the promised lands.
When one day, the job will be finished.
We will hold our hands up and shout,
'I see the promised land!'

Freedom
    and justice!

**Asha Jimale (10)**
**Hambrough Primary School, Southall**


# Valentine's Day

The sun will shine,
The grass will die,
All will be forgotten
But never will I,
Roses are red,
Violets are blue,
This poem is just for you!
Your lips look like raspberries,
Your hair is oh so curly,
You're the very one for me.

*Happy Valentine's Day!*

**Karishma Fatania (9)**
**Hambrough Primary School, Southall**

# Pumpkin, Pumpkin

Pumpkin, pumpkin
Where have you been?
I have been to kill the king.
Pumpkin, pumpkin
How did it go?
It was very fun!

**Vinojan Vigneswaran (8)**
**Hambrough Primary School, Southall**

# Sunset

As Lucy and Tom
sat by the sun
The sun glimmered
Lucy's eyes sparkled
Tom's eyes glowed
The stars glittered
as it fell upon them
They can see two birds
chirping away charmingly
They can smell the
fresh air as it
swirled around them
They can hear the
whispers of a tree
as the wind
drew it back and forth
And also another smell
from over there
a smell of
rose and romance
in the air.

**Nada Ahmed (10)**
**Hambrough Primary School, Southall**

# The Man In Black

The thunder cracked
as the midnight wolf lurked in the shadows
as he jumped in the nearby farm
and slayed three helpless sheep.

The wolf licked his lips which were
smothered in a coat of blood,
all that was left of the sheep
was wool, the size of a cotton bud.

Then a horse came and
chomped on the damp grass,
the ear-piercing screech heard all around
which made the distant birds flee.

The wolf caught them in his sight
and fiercely ran towards them.
The man in black ran around the
corner to St Elms.

The man was out of sight
but only for moments to come,
and there he was, behind him,
with a dagger and a gun.

Just as he shot, the wolf went
around the corner,
sirens sounded, police came
and frightened the wolf away.

The man in black ran
back to his hideout,
he tiptoed in the shadows
and shan't be seen,
his face is a hidden icon,
he's the man in black.

**Jehpal Jhita (10)**
**Hambrough Primary School, Southall**

# Oh, South Africa, How Beautiful You Are!

I stood on the banks of Westbrook
As a canopy of clouds ascended.
I could hear the echoes of the waves
As they smacked the banks.
I could feel the dazzling sand running between my toes.
I could smell the tender meat cooking on the braai stand.
While the golden ball rose out of the clouds
And blazed upon the dolphins' backs
As the warm breeze gently blew against my face
And as the stars glistened in the twilight.

Oh, South Africa, how beautiful you are!

**Parthik Vaghela  (10)**
**Hambrough Primary School, Southall**


# Sunset

Sitting on the icy Table Top
Mountain,
Gazing at the constellation
Above,
I saw the sky turning from
Ocean-blue to blood-red,
The remaindor of the sun
Was reflecting into my sky-blue eyes,
I heard the calmness
Of the waves on
The beach,
The sun looked spectacular,
The more you looked at it the more
It went away from you,
Life is short
But to enjoy it, view a
Sunset in
*South Africa!*

**Iqra Bhatti  (10)**
**Hambrough Primary School, Southall**

# Pussy Cat!

Pussy cat, you are fat.
You are in my hat.
Pussy cat, you are good.
Did you eat my hood?

Pussy cat, don't run away.
You are in my way.
Pussy cat, you saw the sun.
Then ate my chocolate bun.

Pussy cat, you are in the hill.
Your friend was doing the bill.
Pussy cat, you went on a boat
With my coat.

Pussy cat, you have a book.
It is all about Cook.
Pussy cat, you are in love.
I am above you.

Pussy cat, you are lazy.
I am going crazy.
Pussy cat, you are long.
I sang a lovely song.

Pussy cat, you fell down.
Your face is a frown.
Pussy cat, when you fell
I rang the bell.

**Agalya Rajendran  (9)**
**Hambrough Primary School, Southall**

# The Haunted House

In the hallway there is
mysterious knights with axes,
paint peeling off creepy paintings,
rats scattering
and the only sound is thunder
echoing.

In the cellar is
a pile of rotten bones,
a trunk with unwanted, really rusty equipment,
a dusty and cracked mirror
and the sound is the rain leaking
through the cracked walls.

In the kitchen is
sharp knives levitating in the air,
woodlice chewing into the worktop,
ants leading to the fridge
and the only sound is blood being washed
off the knives.

In the attic is
cobwebs everywhere,
rats living in broken floorboards
and the only sound is the floorboards
moving.

**Amar Cheema  (11)**
**Hambrough Primary School, Southall**

# Leave The Dolphins Alone, Please!

Leave the dolphins alone, please!
They don't do anything wrong;
They swim in every ocean
And fill them with their beautiful song.

Leave the dolphins alone, please!
Like us humans they have a brain;
But if we don't start using ours
We won't see them again.

Leave the dolphins alone, please!
We need them in the seas;
We need their life and beauty
And all they need is peace.

Leave the dolphins alone, please!
Let them live their lives;
Let them leap, swim and sing -
Let the dolphins survive.

**Sophia Shire  (9)**
**Hambrough Primary School, Southall**


# The Beach

Lee was swimming
in the sea.
Palm trees are
in the breeze.
I touched the
sand with my
hand.
The key was
in the sea.
People bathing
in the sun.
Children having
lots of
fun.

**Sareena Bassi  (8)**
**Hambrough Primary School, Southall**

# The Haunted House

The attic, old boxes
wind blowing in
from the window
leaves rustling from
outside
people screaming
gives the fright.

The kitchen has
the dark effect
with a foul smell
that makes you
sleepy.

The cellar creaks
after a few weeks
when you stand on
the top.

**Maninder S Matharu  (11)**
**Hambrough Primary School, Southall**


# Friends

Hot and sunny day
Walking In the town
Found a friend of mine.
Walking to the beach
Two kids playing together
As good friends should.
I asked them what
Were their names?
'Tim and Jim,' they said
Quietly, I wish I had
Kids like them.

**Jatinder Dub  (10)**
**Hambrough Primary School, Southall**

# The Haunted House

I entered the cellar and saw
a broken chair with spiders and rats,
cobwebs were all around
and so were the flying bats.

I walked further and entered the attic
and saw a corner full of rat holes,
somewhere were tiny moles,
a wrinkled hosepipe was lying there
and I could hear noises everywhere.

Further out I entered the hallway
and found a long, wide table full of dust,
cobwebs there was a must,
chandeliers were on the wall
and the candles were all over the hall.

Last of all, back in the garden
were some old things
that seemed like they had been used
and then thrown away.
Nothing seemed so scary before . . .

**Preet Kaur  (11)**
**Hambrough Primary School, Southall**


# Seaside

S plashing in the sea,
E at hot dogs with me.
A dolphin swimming with a whale,
S ee the shark's tail.
I n the beachy land,
D ogs sit in the sand.
E xciting at the beach.

**Jaipreet Birdi  (8)**
**Hambrough Primary School, Southall**

# The Haunted House

In the hallway hung a portrait
of a handsome young man
sitting on a huge, posh chair.
The wooden floor was broken
with splinters sticking out
and a dead rat lying aside.

The hallway lead to a steep,
wooden staircase to a cellar
which was dark and dusty
with cobwebs all around.
All that was there as a shattered
window and an old chest of drawers.

Back up the creaking stairs
stood a once glistening, rusty suit of armour
with a spider crawling out of a loose joint.

Further on was a tall, rusty gate
with skeletons lying beside it.
It was dark and gloomy inside.
The gate screeched open
and a swarm of bats flew out.
On the ceiling hung a half-
broken chandelier.
It was a dungeon.

There were little rooms with a tiny
window and gates in front of them.

**Asna Hassam  (11)**
**Hambrough Primary School, Southall**

# The Haunted House

'Look at that house!
It's a haunted house!'
Who said that?
The haunted bat.
Look at those wines
With wavy lines!

*The hall:*
    Rats running
    Someone humming
    Old pictures on the wall
    With paint coming off.

*The kitchen:*
    Spiders crawling on the pans
    2 wings gone from the fan
    Taps covered with blood
    And in the sink there is mud.

*Attic:*
    Trunks full of junk
    The cold air fighting the broken windows
    To come in the room.
    Dead rats
    In the pots.

*Dungeon:*
    There is a dragon in the dungeon
    With sword in the neck.
    Head cut off.
    It is cold too.

**Kanika Khurana (11)**
**Hambrough Primary School, Southall**

# The Haunted House

In the hallway is a
grandfather clock which stopped ticking ages ago,
a crooked armchair which keeps making a squeaky sound,
a picture of a person moving his head side to side,
and the only noise you can hear is the squeaking of the armchair.

In the attic is a plant growing out of the ceiling without any water, air or
light, bats flying around everywhere, broken cobwebs
and rats and the only noise you can hear
is the squeaking of the deadly rats.

In the cellar is an old, rusted bike with only one wheel,
spiders crawling around everywhere
and an old rug that has absorbed a puddle of blood
and the only noise you can hear is the airy wind.

In the dungeon is a skeleton of a human being,
torturing equipment, chains
and the only noise you can hear is the chain
whacking against the walls and a person screaming.

**Preeti Singh (11)**
**Hambrough Primary School, Southall**


# My Family

Ten children lying in bed
Nine aunties cooking Fred
Eight monkeys eating bread
Seven daddies losing their heads
Six brothers hitting others
Five bees eating leaves
Four people knocking on doors
Three spiders crawling up my back
Two babies drinking wine
One I love you Mum.

**Harpreet Nanua (10)**
**Hambrough Primary School, Southall**

# The Haunted House

In the dungeon is a rusty, broken rope,
A guillotine with blood on it,
Walls with cracked bricks,
A sack full of bones
And the only sound is a loud zap of thunder.

In the hallway is a rocking chair with a broken leg,
Antique pictures with paint peeling off,
A chandelier with dusty jewels,
A dark, carpeted, narrow path
And the only sound is the tapping of people walking.

In the cellar is a bicycle with one wheel,
A box of ornaments which are broken,
A pair of cobwebs,
A cracked box full of junk
And the only sound is the swishing of the wind.

In the attic is a wooden plank covered in cobwebs,
Bats making eerie sounds,
Rats scurrying on the floorboards,
Unwanted objects
And the only sound is the bats flying in the air.

**Bijesh Patel  (11)**
**Hambrough Primary School, Southall**


# Come On, It's Snowing

It's snowing,
Let's come and have
Some fun.
It's white like an ice cream when you eat it,
It's like clouds upon me,
If I look at it, it feels like eating a Milky Way.
We can make a snowman,
The snowflake drops on my eyelashes, I blink, they disappear.
The more I look, it makes me sing about it and makes me cry.

**Nisa Dhokia  (10)**
**Hambrough Primary School, Southall**

# The Haunted House

In the cellar I see . . .
a photo frame with a washed-out photo,
a wooden chest filled with old books,
a creaking, wooden stool and
a rusted birdcage.
The only noise I can hear is the howling wind.

In the bedroom I see . . .
a dusty bed in the corner,
a wardrobe rattling to and fro,
a chest of drawers and
an old cradle.
The only noise I can hear is the creaking cradle.

In the kitchen I see . . .
a drawer open and close,
a glass break,
a curtain twitch and
a saucepan drop.
The only thing I hear is the slicing of a knife.

In the hallway I can see . . .
a suit of armour raise its spear,
a step cave in,
a bat fly over my head and
a knife being chucked down the stairs.
The only noise I can hear is the door close
as I exit the haunted house.

**Seema Rehinsi (11)**
**Hambrough Primary School, Southall**

# The Haunted House

Look at that house!
It seems haunted!
Come again,
let's have a peep!

The hall was dreadful,
rats scuttering,
mice muttering,
legs stolen,
chairs broken.

The kitchen, spiders cover the atmosphere,
rats reeking,
bees buzzing,
I am nearly out of my flesh.

The attic is creepy
and a chest
with spiders and dead rats.
I've jumped out of my skin.

*Arghhh!*
I'm out of here!
Never visiting another house
again.

**Mohammed Mussa  (11)**
**Hambrough Primary School, Southall**


# Sea Castles

Sea castles are so, so nice
As a princess
They are made of soft sand and ripples of water.
Everywhere around snap, snap, click,
Click goes the cameras
Swish goes the flags in the breeze of the hot, summer sun.

**Ekta Prashar  (7)**
**Hambrough Primary School, Southall**

# The Haunted House

The cellar has
corners of cobwebs and dust,
the old chests are creaking of rust,
the spiders are crawling
and killing the mice,
everything in sight is not
at all nice
and the only sound is the
quietness of a ghost.

The hallways have
pictures of old people in disguise
and the suits of armour are moving their eyes.
The wallpaper is
polka-dotted with tiny, diamond spots.
When the rats are crawling on top of feet,
the only sound you can hear
is the floor creaking in the air.

The kitchen has teapots that float
in the air, the cakes are chopping
themselves while the ghosts are moving the chairs.
The tablecloth is out of place
and the spoons are floating in thin air
and the only thing you can hear is the
sound of a whistling teapot sitting there.

**Manveer Mahal  (10)**
**Hambrough Primary School, Southall**


# The Beach

I am walking on the beach,
Eating my peach,
Feeling the waves under my feet,
I can feel the heat,
Sitting in my seat.

**Kasim Bashir  (8)**
**Hambrough Primary School, Southall**

# The Haunted House!

In the damp, dark cellar
there's a red, dusty suitcase full of musty, coloured rags.
In the corner is a rusty bicycle
with both wheels missing
but through the little window
you can see the trees swirling
and can hear the window shutting.

In the hallway
there are old pictures on the wall,
above is a massive chandelier
and on the floor is a blood-coloured rug
but all you can see and hear are
shadows and footsteps.

Upstairs in the attic
are boxes of old, crinkling bones,
also millions of cobwebs and
just one newly-lit candle, all
you can hear is the ghosts howling.

**Simran Bassi (11)**
**Hambrough Primary School, Southall**


# The Sea

The sea can be white,
The sea can be blue,
The sea can be see-through,
The sea can be deep,
There might be heaps
And children always weep,
The mothers leap
Like they flew fifty feet.

**Sahib Singh Virdee (8)**
**Hambrough Primary School, Southall**

# Things About Me

Stars so bright,
In the light,
Drinking Sprite,
Flying a kite,
My clothes are tight,
I want a bite.

I had to make,
A lovely cake,
I ate it at a lake,
My friend's name is Jake,
He has a rake.

I have a lovely bear,
I take it everywhere,
I don't care,
About my dares,
My friends are unfair,
I have long hair.

I have a dog,
That likes a log,
Whose friend is Frog,
There was a big fog,
Everybody had a job.

I have a pool,
I look cool,
I have a rule,
You have to look like a fool,
To be in my pool.

**Reena Ravichandran  (10)**
**Hambrough Primary School, Southall**

# My Body

My hair is short and black, once I stuck it with Blu-tak.
Under my hair is my brain and it runs as fast as a train.
My eyes are green and make all the girls dream.
Next come my ears, they don't like to hear
The sound of a grizzly bear.
I have a little nose which likes to smell a red rose.
Then comes my mouth which is wide
And can swallow a great big tide.
My face is dotty and spotty.
My neck holds my head which is always ready for bed.
My shoulders like to slump when they're in a mad hump.
I have very long arms which are good for working on a farm.
At the end of my arms are my hands which like to play with sand.
My lungs are in my chest, they never have a rest.
My heart is my best part, it gives me a good start.
My stomach is small like a round ball.
My intestines are short and l-o-n-g, I hope they don't go wrong.
My kidneys are near my back, they are like great big sacks.
My muscles are strong, just like King Kong.
My bones are tougher than sticks and stones.
My blood is red and bright, what a sight.
My fingers help me pick, they're like little sticks.
My thighs are large, they always need a massage.
My knees are rough as trees.
My skin is still thin.
Next are my ankles that do all the dancing and prancing.
My heels are hard as steel.
My feet do the walking just as good as talking.
My toes like to do a little wiggle and a tiggle.
My skin all over is thin.
Veins run through my body like bristles of rain.
This is a poem about my walking, talking, sleeping body.

**Varudeep Singh Lehal (10)**
**Hambrough Primary School, Southall**

# Colours

Blue is the colour of the sky
Black is when someone dies.

Aqua is the colour of a flood
Red is the colour of blood.

Grey is the colour of a bunny
Gold is the colour of honey.

Green is the colour of grass
Silver is the colour of brass.

Brown is the colour of mud
Pink is the colour of a bud.

Cream is the colour of a bear
White is the colour of fear.

Ginger is the colour of a cat
Purple is the colour of a mat.

**Ranjit Bhandal (10)**
**Hambrough Primary School, Southall**


# Summer

You can swim in summer
You can fly in summer
You can see the sea
The sea making noises
Shhh
You can do biking
You can do hiking.

**Karan Sharma (7)**
**Hambrough Primary School, Southall**

## What Are Friends And Family?

What are family and friends for?
Giving you lots more.
Happy and a lovely life.
Comforting the tears you cry,
Going through times you're shy.
Taking you on lots of breaks
And making home-baked cakes.

Friends support you through hard times,
They hardly ever whine.
Sending you cards on birthdays,
Playing with you on summer days.

My friends and family are the best,
Better than the rest.
They never hurt my feelings.
    That's what friends and families are for.

**Maneesha Sehder  (11)**
**Hambrough Primary School, Southall**


## The Sea

Sea here,
Sea there,
Sea everywhere,
See that sea?
What a scene!

Ships going to the sea,
Ships coming back,
How many ships will there be?

**Leslie Galstaun  (8)**
**Hambrough Primary School, Southall**

# Time Machine

Once upon a rhyme
I rolled back time,
I pressed a button
That looked rather rotten,
It took me to the 80s,
It took me to the 70s,
It took me everywhere
But not the 60s.

The clock wasn't really old
But when my sister went near it
It made her quite bald.

After that she never went near the machine
And the next day
She got chased out of her limousine.

The time machine got older
But I still kept a record in a folder.
A mad scientist saw my machine
And wanted me in his team.

He took my machine
And pressed a button.
He travelled to the 80s
And 70s
But never returned after that.

**Dizare Stuptsik (10)**
Hambrough Primary School, Southall

# Seaside

Going to the seaside
Going to the seaside on a sunny day.
Hip, hip hooray, play with a Frisbee today.
I have to hop, hop, hop.
Football is good for you and me.

**Karanveer Panesar (7)**
Hambrough Primary School, Southall

# Strays

There was a stray which I found on my road
I took it home
I took good care of him
I fed him and cleaned him
One day he ran away from me
The seasons changed as I looked for him
I did everything to find him
But still no luck
I remembered the days when he was there
I grew older but nothing came
I saw the animals but no stray
The day I had waited for him to come had passed away
I waited and waited until the day
Then my stray was back
It was a stray no longer!

**Faris Khan (11)**
**Hambrough Primary School, Southall**


# My Game Boy

I play my Game Boy.
it's so much fun.
I've got lots of games,
most of them are lame
because my sister scratched
off the names.
The rest of the games are anything
but lame.
They're so good I can't put them down.
They're so good I'm holding one right now.
It's proper fun playing Game Boy.
Nothing else can compare.

**Amninder Singh Sangha (11)**
**Hambrough Primary School, Southall**

# Winter

Winter is my favourite season because you get to throw snowballs
                                        at your sister and brothers.
Throw, throw and throw a snowball at the window.
Throw a snowball at your face.
Throw a snowball at your shoelace.

**Mandeep Kaur Gill (8)**
**Hambrough Primary School, Southall**

# Hip-Hop Summer

In the summer I was sweatin'
Cos I was messin'

Wid my homies
Who went to tony's

To get some ice cream
To stop their mouths from dryin'

Dat's very natural
You know it's factual

After dat we were playin' football
Da score was 3-all

We won
Then Mum said, 'Come along.'

We went to da park
We played 'til it was dark

Every day we played
We all said, 'Yay.'

At the last day of summer
It was so much funner

Then it was night
We all said, 'Bye

Until next year.'
My friends said, 'Oh yeah.'

**Jordan Bains (9)**
**Hambrough Primary School, Southall**

# Waves

W ater going whoosh
A ll the time
V isiting the people every time
E xcited people in the sea
S plash!

**Parabhjeet Sunner (8)**
**Hambrough Primary School, Southall**

# A Dream

I was dreaming that I was
flying into the sky,
with seagulls flying. I saw,
I saw my brother crying,
down below me. I saw someone
frying. My mum screamed,
'Come down or else I'll come
and get you.' I screamed, I
screamed, 'Mum, give me a
clue of what to do.'

'Hurry, hurry, I want you to come down
or I'll turn you into a clown.'
'Mum, Mum, I can't take it anymore,
you're too slow.' A white seagull
flew into the water and it flipped
as it went in.

The waves were rushing one by one
against the seagull's beak and feet.
I felt like I had great big wings.
Beneath my feet, I could see children
playing with swings. At last my wings
became arms and I was back to normal
after all. Suddenly I came down and landed
on two feet, I never want to fly, not even
in my dream.

**Hifsa Shaukat (11)**
**Hambrough Primary School, Southall**

# Seaside And Waves

S wimming all the time
E ating hot dogs in the sun
A ll the kids playing
S plashing in the sea
I ce cream is the best
D ive in the sea
E veryone is hot.

W ater splashing everywhere
A ll the people getting wet
V ery happy
E xcited children
S wimming in the sea.

**Nikhil S Sohal  (8)**
**Hambrough Primary School, Southall**


# Mr Pirate

Ms Pirate
Has a parrot
Who lives
In a parrot
House.
Mr Pirate
Has a
Parrot
Who lives in
An old
Ship and
Who travels
In the deep water.

**Banuja Balendran  (8)**
**Hambrough Primary School, Southall**

## Sharks

S ome people
H ave hot dogs
A nd some people have drinks
R achel is kind, so
K ind that she always
S hares her things.

**Renu Rehinsi (8)**
**Hambrough Primary School, Southall**


## Seaside Poems

Seaside, seaside come to the sand.
Seaside, seaside, there is a sandcastle.
Splashing in a sea
That's where all the people are.
Seashore, seashore, the creatures
Are coming from the trees
Going on a shore where people sit down.

**Mandeep Singh (8)**
**Hambrough Primary School, Southall**


## The Snow Poem

It's snowing
It's snowing
White as snow
Let us see the snow
Let us see the fun
Let us see the sun
Fading in the sky
And never seeing it again
Until the end of April.

**Maryam Aden (10)**
**Hambrough Primary School, Southall**

# Sea Creatures

I like sea creatures,
They hate me.
I hate sand,
They like sand.

I like ice cream,
They hate ice cream.
I hate the sea,
They like the sea.

I like the pier,
They hate the pier,
I like the promenade,
They hate the promenade.

I like people,
They hate people . . .
They eat you if they see you!
*Watch out when you're at sea!*

**Sumaya Jumale (8)**
**Hambrough Primary School, Southall**


# The Seaside

In the sea you can swim
You can make a sandcastle
You can sometimes buy ice cream
In the seaside you can sit on deckchairs
You can catch a wave
You can have a drink
In the seaside you can lie down.

**Mandeep Nanua (8)**
**Hambrough Primary School, Southall**

# Seaside

Seaside, seaside, what a wonderful sight,
Seaside, seaside, what a wonderful flight,
Play on the seashore,
Like the great core,
The new sea,
The old sea,
Going to the seaside on a
Sunny day,
Hip! Hip! Hooray!
Me and my brother Lee are
Going to the seaside,
To visit the sea,
Sand, sand, sand is so hot,
That people jump on the
Spot,
We sit on a donkey,
Who laughs like a monkey.

**Rameez Mussa (8)**
**Hambrough Primary School, Southall**

# I Wish

I wish I was a fish
Who could swim in a dish
I wish I was a fairy
Named Mary
Who lived in a dairy!
I wish, I wish . . .

**Nushida Soni (8)**
**Hambrough Primary School, Southall**

# Flowers

Roses so red, violets so blue,
So sweet-smellling, just like you,
Buttercups, sunflowers and poppies too,
Types of flowering blooms.

Scents so nice,
Petals so delicate,
Some big, some small
But still all flowering blooms.

Colourful petals,
Bright green stems,
Dandelions, tulips and jasmines,
All flowering blooms.

Bright blue, bright pink, all colours,
Different colours but all still flowers,
Blossom going through spring, dying through winter,
Are all flowering blooms.

**Yasmeen Bashir (10)**
**Hambrough Primary School, Southall**

# Pumpkin, Pumpkin

Pumpkin, pumpkin
Where have you been?
I've been to Hallowe'en
To frighten the queen.
Pumpkin, pumpkin,
How did you do?
I did fine, thank you.
Skeleton, skeleton,
Where are you?
I'm under the bed
Do you know?
No, you're not.
I'm invisible right now.

**Gurshran Sandhu (8)**
**Hambrough Primary School, Southall**

# About Me

Football player
Money maker
Goal scorer
Serious spender
God lover
Bible reader
School hater
Drum player
Play maker
Saha lover
Bike rider
Story teller
MC rapper
Man U lover
Millwall hater
Football lover
Joke teller.

**Tony Osei-Sarfo  (11)**
**Herbert Morrison School, London**


# The School Zoo

The school is a zoo,
Locking children up until three-thirty,
The school is a feeding ground,
Feeding ravenous children,
The school is an exercising ground,
Gradually sucking energy out of the energetic children,
The school is like a zoo,
Children fighting over territory.

**Christopher Yankson**
**Herbert Morrison School, London**

# The World Around Us

This new world is confusing,
People killing animals,
War breaking out everywhere,
People vomiting out graffiti,
Murders, kidnapping children,
Thieves rich in emeralds and diamonds,
I am going *insane*,
Watching people die,
Now that hate controls us
And soon I am going to be dead.

**Lawrence Esan  (11)**
**Herbert Morrison School, London**


# All About Me

Football lover
School hater
Goal scorer
Bike rider
Good speller
Never quitter
Money spender
Bible prayer
God lover
Joke teller
Money maker
Henry lover
Sun liker
Rain hater
Music lover.

**Luke Kechane  (11)**
**Herbert Morrison School, London**

# Prison

Me and my friend are all alone,
15 minutes ago I was on the phone.
All we get is chicken and rice,
I have dandruff, he has lice.
I got nicked for daylight robbery,
He got nicked for killing a man in a lorry.
I lived with my mother, he lived with his wife.
I'm in here for 15 years, my friend is in here for life.

**Elisabeth Clarke (12)**
**Herbert Morrison School, London**


# Desert Predator

I looked out over the horizon,
To spy a tiny speck,
It kept on moving,
On its endless trek,
Waiting for an animal to fall in the heat,
Then it will start its downward dive,
And when the vulture lands it will meet,
Others of its kind enjoying the feast.

**Liam Lawrence Stephens (11)**
**Herbert Morrison School, London**


# Fire Engines

Roaring in frustration
Waiting for the signal
Escaping from the station
Even at nightfall
Stomping down the city streets
On its way, bawling
Alerting everyone it meets
Before death starts calling.

**Michael Asare (11)**
**Herbert Morrison School, London**

# A Rosey Riddle

Careful, they're sharp,
The bee's music is as sweet as a harp,
Vivid red or pink,
They never make your heart sink,
Even if they prick,
The time will still tick,
You get this gift on Valentine's,
They ask, 'Will you be mine?'

*Rose.*

**Seniz Kasif (11)**
**Herbert Morrison School, London**


# The Breeze

The breeze is as gentle as silk,
it runs all over your body
and tickles your toes,
the breeze is as cold as ice.

It sways to and fro,
it rustles the leaves on any tree,
the breeze is a special thing to me,
it blows me away.

*I love the breeze!*

**Lauren Alison Jardine (11)**
**Herbert Morrison School, London**


# Our World - Cinquain

Sad is
Our world because
Of all the killing and
Abuse to our animals. Why?
Let's stop!

**Andrew Aikins (11)**
**Herbert Morrison School, London**

# How Romantic? Not! - Cinquain

It's love
Really is love
Always flows in the sky
Oh no, it's not love it's danger
That's life.

**Oluwaseun Adeite  (11)**
**Herbert Morrison School, London**


# Silent Graveyard

Out in the graveyard my feet crunching on the leaves,
Pitch-black, I cannot see,
Waiting for my dad, has he forgotten me?
Freezing cold I can see my own breath,
Spirits surrounding me, surrounded by death,
Voices in my head,
I wish I was dead,
I am really scared,
*Where are you, Dad?*

**Jason Kerrane  (11)**
**Herbert Morrison School, London**


# Kennings

Joke killer
Good learner
Sport player
Food eater
Dog hater
Money lover
Egg hater
Book reader
Good speaker
Goal scorer
Football player.

**Zakee Wilson  (11)**
**Herbert Morrison School, London**

# The Treasures Of Nature

When the sun comes up every day
The treasures of nature are unleashed.

The birds start singing with the breeze
The bees start to buzz in the trees
The frogs start jumping on the leaves
Butterflies begin to swoop through the breeze

And when the sun falls from the sky
The moon rises over the trees and
The treasures fall asleep.

When the moon comes up every night
The treasures of nature are unleashed.

The mighty bat swoops through the air x-raying its prey.
The owl flies through the air softly but disguises itself
It is really a devil.

The squeaky mouse runs away from the ripping owl
And the powerful wolf beams its prey with its sharp teeth.

When the moon catapults from the sky
And the sun beams over the horizon
The night treasures fall asleep.

Nature circles around and starts another day.

**Joshua Emm  (8)**
**Highwoods Primary School, Colchester**


# The Queen Of Autumn

I am the queen of autumn,
Juicy red berries I adore.
I make the leaves fall from the trees
And scatter them all over the floor.

I am the queen of autumn,
I sit on my golden throne.
Until the king of winter comes
And claims it as his own.

**Chloe Rutland  (8)**
**Highwoods Primary School, Colchester**

# Rapping Gran

She rapped in the playgrounds, she rapped near the pond,
Her wig flew off and she showed she was bald.
She rapped to cats and to dogs,
She rapped to the penguins and then to the frogs.
As she went I made myself clean
And watched her singing *'I'm A Rip-Rap Queen'*.

She danced to the Queen, performed to the mayor,
Danced with the president and then Tony Blair.
She rapped up the steps, woke the street,
She clapped her hands and stamped her feet.
As she went she made a crowd
But she sang there and quite loud.

She rapped in the courtyard and then in the zoo,
Saw the cows and made them moo.
Went to Africa, saw monkeys too,
As she went she saw snakes too.
She even taught piranhas mean,
Ten out of ten for the *Rip-Rap Queen!*

**James Taylor  (9)**
**Highwoods Primary School, Colchester**


# Growing Up

When I grow up
I would like to be
A pirate on the
Deep, blue sea.

**Liam Mair  (7)**
**Highwoods Primary School, Colchester**

# The Listening Walk

Inside
Children talking,
Grown-ups telling,
Mrs Woraker laughing,
Voices shouting,
Computer keys clicking,
Printer humming,
Curtains rushing,
Water splashing,
Click the lid,
Phone ringing,
Paper turning,
Drawer opening - squeak!
Draw closing - *bang!*
'Excuse me,' said Mr Milner.

Outside
Wind whooshing,
Children's voices,
A bus,
Songs on the radio,
Fridge humming,
Extractor fan breathing,
Sparrows cheeping,
Aeroplane zooming,
Footsteps walking,
Crow croaking,
Tyres creaking,
Tyres squeaking,
Door banging.
*Bang!*

**A Year 1 Class Poem**
**Highwoods Primary School, Colchester**

# Wings

If I had wings
I would touch the candyfloss clouds across the world.

If I had wings
I would taste the sizzling hot sun warming up everybody.

If I had wings
I would breathe deep and sniff the smoke from the kitchen houses everywhere.

If I had wings
I would gaze at the people walking around town.

If I had wings
I would dream of discovering the world again.

**Tiia Barkham  (9)**
**Highwoods Primary School, Colchester**

# Untitled

He goes in hard
And always comes out on top
Of the game.
He spits when he talks,
Kicks anyone that walks,
He's Irish Rock
Who knocks off people's blocks.
He's always getting suspended
But he comes back respected!
He's the captain of Man United,
Against Madrid is the only game
Where he gets excited.

**Lewis Percival  (10)**
**Highwoods Primary School, Colchester**

# The Runaway Zoo

We have all heard of the Runaway Bride
But this is different you see,
Because if you throw in a pig and you throw in a horse
And you throw in a boat and the sea,
Then you get a slimy snake
And grab a cool cat too
With an enormous elephant sat at the back,
Then, hey, you've a Runaway Zoo.
So there they were, a hat for a boat,
Hungry, their throats sore and dry
But their luck changed, came out of the blue,
Eight bananas floating by
And they sailed and sailed day and night,
'Til they found an abandoned house,
Right there in the middle of the sea
On an island all small like a mouse.
'Hooray,' shouted the horse.
'We're saved,' said the cat.
'No we're not,' cried the pig.
'There's a hole in our hat!'

**Tiffany Reeves (11)**
**Highwoods Primary School, Colchester**


# The Flower

One morning a flower came
The leaves were pointed like a corner of paper
The roots were as hairy as a carpet
The petals were rounded like a circle.

**Sam Cullis (7)**
**Highwoods Primary School, Colchester**

# Spring

The clouds drift and race along the sky,
A big bunch of candyfloss in the corner of my eye.

I can feel the wind on my bare cheeks
And the trees are swaying in the breeze.

Pansies smiling back at me
And gaze at the sun joyfully.

Beautiful purple crocus like amethyst
With the smell of a cold winter evening.

White cotton wool dangling from the branches,
Delightful parts of a delicate whipped cream.

Willy Wonker's furry caterpillars
Trying to escape the trees and bushes.

Rosemary with the stench of a warm, summer night
Is so beautiful, I'm filled with delight.

Birds tweet as if a whistle at the end of a football match.
Spring is here, spring is back!

**Kat Waring (10)**
**Highwoods Primary School, Colchester**

# A Spell To Make Teachers Vanish

Take four legs from a spiral millipede.
Next find seven rotten toenails.
Mix carefully with a pinch of salt.
Then put in as many gruesome rats' tails as you can find.
Be slow or else you will change into a rat.
Use a long spoon and carefully stir.
Add crumbs of battered human skull.
Finally leave it in the yellow moonlight
Until the dreaded werewolf howls.
Give only to teachers.

**Luke Chapman (8)**
**Highwoods Primary School, Colchester**

# Spring Poem

Slowly peeping,
The white, cotton blossom buds,
Come to life.
Daffodils open up
Like a baby caterpillar brooding.
The smell of spring air
Is summer
At the beach.
Lavender
Is a smooth, downy bed.
Pansies,
Look at you, with a big smile on their faces.
The berries
Are as ruby as a grazed knee.
The clouds
Are the sheep,
Cuddly, soft tails.
The winds
Blow south-easterly
And the breeze
Is taking me
With it.
A bunch of narcissi
Facing the sun
And bowing down,
The purple jewels of crocuses
Looking back at me,
Flowing in the wind.
Spring is here?
So enjoy it!

**Phoebe Connell  (11)**
**Highwoods Primary School, Colchester**

# The Van To Glasgow

This is the man in his van
On his trip to Glasgow.

This is the traffic jam
That caused the man in the van
To slow down on his trip to Glasgow.

This is the orange, stripy cone
And his little mobile phone,
The traffic jam
That caused the man in the van
To slow down on his trip to Glasgow.

This is the traffic light
At the dead of night,
This is the orange, stripy cone
And his little mobile phone,
The traffic jam
That caused the man in the van
To slow down on his trip to Glasgow.

This is the mad car driver
Called Peter Fiver,
The traffic light
At the dead of night,
The orange, stripy cone
And his little mobile phone,
The traffic jam
That caused the man in the van
To slow down on his trip to Glasgow.

At the crack of dawn
The driver made a little yawn
To remember . . .
The mad car driver
Called Peter Fiver,
The traffic light
At the dead of night,

The orange, stripy cone
And his little mobile phone,
The traffic jam
That caused the man in the van
To slow down on his trip to Glasgow.

**Stuart Clarke  (11)**
**Highwoods Primary School, Colchester**


# Garden Flower

Roots are smelly like a dustbin
Roots are all dark brown
Stems are all wet at the bottom
Stems are all dark green
Petals are all silver
Petals are all smooth
Leaves are all smooth, shiny and bright green
Flowers are all beautiful and shiny
Flowers are pink and rainbow colours.

**Jade Bond  (7)**
**Highwoods Primary School, Colchester**


# Loud Explosion

It is an explosion of flashing, beautiful, glittery stars and ashes.
It is a wonder of brightness and colour.
It's a wonderful explosion like the smell of dampness,
Decay and rot.
It's got silver and gold sparkling light.
It's like a tiger going to explode in your eyes
And give you a big growl
And a snake going higher and higher.

**Baha Abdullah  (10)**
**Highwoods Primary School, Colchester**

# My Dog

I love my dog, he plays with me
He is as cute as cute can be.

He's a golden nugget, soft and fun
He's a pouncing part of the sun.

He's my baby, I love him
I will never throw him in the bin.

He jumps round into a tree, he comes
And runs and jumps on me.

I love him
And he loves
Me!

**Zoe Hammond  (10)**
**Highwoods Primary School, Colchester**


# My Pretty Flower

My pretty flower is light pink
My pretty flower is special
My pretty flower is gentle
My pretty flower is big
My pretty flower is tall
My pretty flower is lovely
My pretty flower is colourful
My pretty flower is soft
My pretty flower is smooth.

**Hannah McCarthy  (7)**
**Highwoods Primary School, Colchester**


# The Moon Is Like . . .

The moon is like a robin flying in the air.
The moon is like a cloud floating in the sky.
The moon is like a blackbird flying in the garden.

**Tom Wolstenholme  (6)**
**Highwoods Primary School, Colchester**

# Good And Evil

Good and Evil, it's always the same
Good triumphs over Evil, it's so lame
But what would happen if it all goes the wrong way?
There would be chaos, madness, that's what I'll say
There would be trees getting burnt down
Fires all around
The streets wouldn't be safe
Criminals escaped
No one to rely on
Everyone to spy on
That's what the world would be like if it all goes the wrong way.

**Ayrand Cruz  (10)**
**Highwoods Primary School, Colchester**


# In The Car

When Mum drives, all Dad ever does is . . .
Neck nuzzling,
Crossword puzzling,
Toe picking,
Bogey flicking,
Mum snogging,
Bog hogging,
Loud snoring,
Extremely boring,
Shopping getting,
List forgetting,
Slightly greying . . .

    *Dad!*

**Holly Davies  (10)**
**Highwoods Primary School, Colchester**

# Seven Ways Of Looking At My Mum!

A shouting machine that's gone terribly wrong.
A cuddly teddy bear like your favourite one.
A loving heart who's gentle and kind.
A cooking cook who's sweet inside.
A household chorer, she's not a snorer.
She's my only mum and she never rests.
She's the mum that's the *best!*

**Emilie Findlay (11)**
**Highwoods Primary School, Colchester**


# Autumn

The windmill turning
Hard to produce flour.
The fields full of wheat,
Crops and barley.
The shiny, brown conkers
Trapped inside their spiky shells.
The red and gold leaves
Crunching as I walk through them.
The river frozen like ice.

**Melissa Warnes (7)**
**Highwoods Primary School, Colchester**


# Swimming With A Shark

Splish, splish
Splash, splash
Crunch, crack
Punch, smack
Munch, hack
Twisted leg
Twisted head
Oh no, you're dead!

**Lewis Howe (9)**
**Highwoods Primary School, Colchester**

# In The Bath

Splash, gurgle,
Bath time is fun,
Splish, splosh,
I hope I'm never done.
Time to get out,
Drip, dribble,
Oh no, wrinkled skin!
Squish, squish.

**Lewis Bailey (10)**
**Highwoods Primary School, Colchester**


# Underwater World

Underwater so full of life.
Full of spirit, fun and might.
Full of fish, sharks and shells.
Full of seaweed waving with life.
Just like a world made for me.
Jewels and treasure all for me.
Sand at the bottom and
Sparkling shells.

Glittering pearls
And a golden oyster.
A little starfish so kind and red.
A little green mermaid
So soft and slimy
But with golden eyes,
She's just my friend.

**Lucinda Conder (8)**
**Norland Place School, London**

# The Sea

The beach is my favourite place to be
With swishing waves that come to me.

The sea swishes, glitters and has a gleam
And turns the night to a wonderful dream.

The shells fill my ear with the sound of the sea
I think there's an island inside
As small as a pea.

**Helena Williams  (8)**
**Norland Place School, London**


# The London Eye

The London Eye is like a wheel
It goes round and round
And when you get to the top
It sometimes makes you shiver.
It is surrounded by buildings
And is held over the Thames
So people think you can fall in!
It is like you're in a bubble!
But it does not *pop!*

**Eléonore Gomm  (8)**
**Norland Place School, London**


# The Shell

In my ear
With a shell held near
I am on the beach
The sea close enough to reach.
The waves are loud
And there's shells to be found
And the sea's as blue as the sky.

**Chloe Smith  (8)**
**Norland Place School, London**

# At The Aquarium

At the aquarium I saw grinning sharks
with white teeth that could bite you at any time.
I wish I could dive in and floss them!
I saw turtles stacked on top of each other like a pile of bricks.
I could build a house of turtles
and my house would swim across the sea!
I touched the backs of the stingrays
which were as spiky as a crocodile
but I was so amazed their bellies were as soft as velvet.
The fish were happy but sad too.

They swim round, round, all day, all night.
Just think of them and they are still there.

I'd like to swim with them across the ocean
to where the moon touches the water!

**Josie Whitley (8)**
**Norland Place School, London**


# I Love The Pufferfish

At the aquarium we saw some baby turtles
And lots of fishes too,
We touched the stingrays and they felt funny,
They were spongy and slimy - *eeeeoooo!*
The sharks were amazing, spotty, big and small
But I like the pufferfish best of all!

When we went to the aquarium we saw a stingray say, 'Hello,'
And a really bright fish that was purple and yellow,
We saw a baby shark, it was really, really small
But I like the pufferfish best of all!

**Elsie Hewitt (8)**
**Norland Place School, London**

# What I Hear In My Ear

A
shell
that
sounds like
the sea.

The waves that
crash against the shore.

The stones that are in different shapes.

The crystals that you find
are so shiny
and are gleaming in the sun.

The seagulls that fly
overhead.

That's the
life for
me.

**Lulu Straker (8)**
**Norland Place School, London**


# In A Bubble In The Air

The London Eye is big and round
It's like a giant wheel
From it you can see a fisherman
Pulling up his reel.

You can see from the Eye
Lots of buildings
Like Parliament, the Queen's house
And all the parks too.

From it a house looks tiny
Almost like a mouse
It really looks absurd that a bird
Is as small as a louse.

**Olivia Bryant (8)**
**Norland Place School, London**

## Midsummer's Night

Behold the mighty shark of waves
Who holds a knife full of glaze.
He takes his knife with all his might
To fight against a dangerous knight
But the knight is strong and the knight is slick
And he has pincers that pinch you 'til you're sick.
They fought all day, they fought all night
Until the shark took a strike.
He hit the crab with all his might
And the crab fell down dead on that midsummer's night.

**Isa Conroy  (8)**
**Norland Place School, London**


## The Octopus

He can open a jar
But can't see very far.
He slowly glides up to me
He simply loves the sea.
I would not lie
Because I saw it with my own eyes.
His slimy 8 legs
I would never dread
If he came up to me
In the sea.

The sea is his home
Even if he is alone.
He does like to roam
About the sea.
It's his home
With me.

**Abigail Hampson  (7)**
**Norland Place School, London**

# The Sweet Sounds In The Sea

I'm sitting on a rock, I feel so cold
I look away, a wave comes down on me
I start to drown, I hear a nice sound
It's a mermaid, I can breathe in the water
I can see my parents in the water playing but
It's night, I wake up, I find I'm dreaming
But I can still hear the sweet sound of the mermaid.

**Olivia Masek  (8)**
**Norland Place School, London**


# Under The Sea

Fishes that swim
Fishes that fly
All different colours but my, oh my
If only I could take one as a pet
I will treat him well
Want to bet?

But then I put him back in the sea
So he can swim with me
And go free.

**Eleonore Decaux  (8)**
**Norland Place School, London**


# Yellow Eel

The yellow eel swam past me
I almost lost my mind
He is freaky and very, very creepy
He slithers over the rocks and stones
    Oh, oh, oh!
        How creepy!

**Matilda Moir  (7)**
**Norland Place School, London**

# The Beach

The sea is blue,
The sun is bright.
The sand is warm.
Fish are swimming
And dolphins are mating
And the gills on a fish are shining brightly.
When you're walking along the beach you can feel
                              the sand in your toes,
And the sun sets as you're walking home.
You can't wait for the next day on the beach and to play games
And build sandcastles out of the beautiful golden sand,
And walk along the pebbles and the shiny shells along the beach,
Tiny sea creatures following you along the beach.

**Lujaine Al-Habib (7)**
**Norland Place School, London**

# Holding A Shell

When I'm standing at the sea
There is a shell by me as beautiful as can be
I pick it up and hold it to my ear
Then I hear the sea again
It seems like it's there in the shell
It sounds like the sea is rushing
Then out leaps a dolphin that shimmers in the light
And then goes back in again
All so exciting
But I can't reach it
So I put it down and walk away
As I'm looking sadly at the bay.

**Zoe Adler (8)**
**Norland Place School, London**

# My Sea Poem

I
went
to the
London
Aquarium.
Oh, it was
a stadium.
When I went
inside it the fish
were swaying to
and fro.
Red, pink, yellow
and blue, ah the
colours fish have
on them.

I went to see
the jellyfish all
bobbing up and
down. It was a lovely night
and goodness,
glee, the jellyfish have come
to me.

**Amy-Laure Richards  (8)**
**Norland Place School, London**

# The Sea

When I am sitting by the sea
See the octopuses far out at sea
And then the jellyfish comes along
With its tentacles so long.

And there is a fish having his lunch
With his shiny tail shining in the sea
But then it is time to go to bed
So I say goodbye to the seabed.

**Jemima Salmon  (7)**
**Norland Place School, London**

# 7 Teachers In 7 Years

In reception I had Miss Blake,
She taught us lots of things to make.

In Year 1 I had Miss Holmshaw,
She taught us about dinosaurs.

In Year 2 I had Miss Henderson,
She taught us about pentagons.

In Year 3 I had Miss Webb,
She hurt her arm so she stayed in bed.

In Year 4 I had Mr Burns,
He taught us about ¾ turns.

In Year 5 I had Miss Nutman,
She was funny, nice, a lovely woman.

In Year 6 I have Miss McWilliams,
She is kind, nice and we like her millions!

**Shauna McKenny (11)**
**Our Lady Of Lourdes RC Primary School, Leigh-On-Sea**

# Wings Of Wisdom

It moves so swift, so fast and so graceful
Cutting through the midnight air.
As It brushes its snow-white wings
Against a subtle tree.
White as the stars perched on its branch
It waits for the sound of prey in
Winter's darkness.
And then, prey calls, it calls back
With its smooth beak.
Then it swoops down so alert and
So careful hunting its prey as it follows
A slender trail.
And it stopped to satisfy its taste
With a chunk of meat as bloody as flames.
An owl.

**Joshua Lewis (11)**
**Our Lady Of Lourdes RC Primary School, Leigh-On-Sea**

# It's A Wonderful Life

Gentle as the wind
Soft as a baby's skin
Pure as a glass of water
And graceful as a dolphin's leap.

One day I wish to become one with the world
And at peace with life on Earth
And our glorious sights and smells.

There is so much in life that needs exploring
And so much for me to discover
And so much more than what meets the eye.

It uncovers itself and opens up our eyes
To what's in life worth living
And not what's worth to ignore.

It shows us more than what we have been taught
And if for once in our life, it's true
The only thing we can ever trust
Is everything will change.

**Laura Baillie  (11)**
**Our Lady Of Lourdes RC Primary School, Leigh-On-Sea**


# If I

If I owned the keys to the Earth,
I would make the sun shine on you and me,
As we always live in shadow,
Happy it would make me be.

If I could change the world,
I would take out all the sorrow,
I would take out all the war
And happiness I would borrow.

If I could ask for just one thing,
I would ask for my nation,
To see that we were made to be one,
Not an arguing creation.

**Liam Peoples  (11)**
**Our Lady Of Lourdes RC Primary School, Leigh-On-Sea**

# Dreams

Dreams are funny, sometimes scary,
As they move around your head,
Some are ones you wish you'd done
And some you wish you would never have had.

Then you wake in the misty black
Wondering why you're out of bed,
Then you think to yourself,
*It must have been that dream I had.*

As you walk back upstairs,
In the jet-black corners you see your fears,
Walking backwards into a wall you turn, trip and fall,
When you get up you hear a creak,
You run back to your bed with a squeak.

When you wake in the morning,
Happy that the sun is shining,
You have no fears to overcome
But what you do fear is the night to come.

**James Seaden (10)**
**Our Lady Of Lourdes RC Primary School, Leigh-On-Sea**


# If

If everyone would learn to love,
If everyone would be kinder,
If everyone would learn to share,
If everyone wanted peace,
If everyone had liberty and freedom,
If everyone would be happy,
If everyone had a place to sleep at night,
If everyone had somebody to love them,
If everyone wanted war to stop,
If everyone stopped hurting each other,
The world would be a better place.

**Laurence Baker (11)**
**Our Lady Of Lourdes RC Primary School, Leigh-On-Sea**

# After The Battle

The King's men victorious, all happy and glorious,
Holding their flag up in glory over the old king.
'Long live the King,' we shouted. King Henry the furious.

I try to remember, all I can hear is the
Sound of horses' hooves,
Our men charging down the hill,
Arrows firing at our men,
Running down the hill with broken Bill.

My heart pounding as we fight at the bottom
Of the hill, the sound of clanging steel,
Sending shivers down my back.
The cavalry getting ready to have their whack
At the enemy's tack.

The next bit is awful,
It looked like a blood stream,
Running across the lands.
The enemy laying wherever we walk.
I wish I hadn't done it, I wish there was peace.

**Karl Sharman (11)**
**Our Lady Of Lourdes RC Primary School, Leigh-On-Sea**


# Shoes!

Red shoes,
Blue shoes,
Yellow shoes,
Pink shoes,
Shoes that have buckles,
Shoes that have laces,
Shoes that slip on,
New shoes,
Old shoes,
Big shoes,
Little shoes!

**Aimee Gargan (8)**
**Our Lady Of Lourdes RC Primary School, Leigh-On-Sea**

# The War . . .

As the sun beats down on my bloody face,
As I lie here in my trench,
Fighting for the country. War will never end.
Bombs smashing, shells crashing
Is all the noise I hear.

My dreams and hopes all fade away.
As I am lying all alone
I close my eyes and think of home.

An open wound across my face,
I may never move from this place,
As I hear the gunfire in my head,
I'm sure I'm going to die.

As I lie here and I close my eyes,
I'm sure there will be a better place,
Instead of lying here with a wounded face.

**Ellen Jeffery (11)**
**Our Lady Of Lourdes RC Primary School, Leigh-On-Sea**

# Where Is The Peace?

What is that in the sky
Falling, passing by?
Oh no, it is a bomb!

Now I know that war has come,
Flames are rising up so high,
Aeroplanes flying by.

Buildings are coming crashing down,
I think the King will lose his crown,
I hope the Germans' fire will cease.

Do you hear the kayseash?
Why did the Germans break their truce?
I wonder . . .
    Where is the peace?

**William Chuck (11)**
**Our Lady Of Lourdes RC Primary School, Leigh-On-Sea**

# My Life

Was born on 5<sup>th</sup> of November,
In the foreground of an enchanted light,
Was born on 5<sup>th</sup> of November,
On the day of Guy Fawkes' night.

Three brothers came before me,
I have a big family you see.

Three older brothers I have,
Dwelling in this congested haven,
Three older brothers I have,
Michael, Graham and Adrian.

At the gallant age of four,
I was yet to be mature.

Each winter from the age of four,
We escape to the ski slopes,
Which I adore,
We race down white, glistening mountain tracks,
Slow down, hockey, stop, then look back.

Approaching the school all nervous and tense,
Waiting for the moment to commence,
The whistle blows,
To class we go.

Going to Upton Park,
To see West Ham United,
Win, lose or draw,
Either way I'm excited.

I'm eleven but almost twelve,
Four years from seven,
My final year at primary school has begun,
I hope not a hard slog and no fun!

Fifteen years from now
I often wonder
Where I will be,
Let's wait and see.

**Xavier Conner  (11)**
**Our Lady Of Lourdes RC Primary School, Leigh-On-Sea**

# Baboon!

One day all the animals
land and sea
decided to meet up
on the land of glee.

And there they sat
in utter despair
when baboon came along
with sand in his hair.

'Would you like some tea?'
he said with a smile
'No thanks,' they said
as they ran a mile.

For the problem they met for
which had come so soon
was quite obvious
it was silly old baboon.

He sailed the sea
or rather the sand
with a hat on his head
and a spoon in his hand.

The reason I know is quite simple really
I'll tell you the reason very clearly
one day I looked into my spoon
I realised quite frankly, I am the baboon.

**Olivia Allen  (10)**
**Our Lady Of Lourdes RC Primary School, Leigh-On-Sea**

# Take A Ride Over Hills And Seas

*(To my mum and family)*

Take a ride over hills and seas,
Try and resist the Lake District breeze,
Watch the mountains,
Shadows deep,
Climb the mountains,
Though they are steep,
When you're there you shall not bore,
Over nature you shall soar,
Over deep grass you shall tread
And walk the path of hidden thread,
See the green grass and the deep, blue lakes,
Watch the robin as he wakes,
So make a wish in the deep wishing well
And for years to come you'll have a story to tell,
So go now, go and don't look back
And walk the maze, the hidden track.

**Niall Purcell (11)**
**Our Lady Of Lourdes RC Primary School, Leigh-On-Sea**

# My Brother

My brother is a pain in the neck,
Sometimes he makes me an angry wreck,
My blood boils like a volcano,
When he calls me a 'lamo same o'!

He always has an angry fit,
When I go shout and hit,
I always like to annoy him thin,
About his spotty skin!

My brother is always up to tricks,
Which really, really, really kicks!
He always is one or t'other
But after all he is my brother!

**Joanna Boosey (11)**
**Our Lady Of Lourdes RC Primary School, Leigh-On-Sea**

# Life Is Quiet Here

As the world begins to change,
Bad rulers are still in reign.
People around us complain about money,
While the Earth decays, it just isn't funny.
No one will help, no one cares,
When you think about who dares,
When creatures die,
No one asks why.
With smoke in the air, birds become rare.
With oil filling water,
Fish become less.
As people ignore what they must hear,
Can't they tell that life is quiet here?

When all life has died out,
Will humans then begin to doubt
Their actions of those years before,
When all the creatures were plenty more?
When death is coming down the hall,
Will people then begin to stall?
Will they regret their actions done,
When the end of the world has begun?
Will they remember the world of old,
When the Earth was bright and bold?
Will they know they were the one,
That threatened the Earth with a gun?
Will people then be able to hear,
That life is always quiet here?

**Sam Ridgeway (11)**
**Our Lady Of Lourdes RC Primary School, Leigh-On-Sea**

# A Poem About Weather

Cold, freezing, frosty, sunny, scorching, perfect, windy and warm.
The summer makes me feel happy, great and wonderful.
The winter makes me feel cold, horrible and rosy.
The spring makes me feel warm, loving and full of happiness.
The autumn makes me feel rosy, windy and crinkly.

**Grace Forrai  (7)**
**Our Lady Of Lourdes RC Primary School, Leigh-On-Sea**


# One Man's Desire

The world is on fire,
Because of one man's desire,
Hitler's his name,
War is his game!

He comes from Hell,
With a sick mind he dwell,
The war is almost won,
Britain is almost done!
Hitler could win,
He's wearing a grin,
Dunkirk is near,
The world is full of fear!

Children are screaming,
The air raid is wailing,
We hate it when the bomb explodes,
Destroying all the homes and roads!

The apocalypse is near,
The priests are filled with fear,
It is Christmas, the world is full of frost,
The world is almost lost . . .

**Max Robinson  (11)**
**Our Lady Of Lourdes RC Primary School, Leigh-On-Sea**

# Mum!

Goldilocks, Goldilocks
How could you dare?
Trespass with no pass,
Nor any care.

Mum, that's not fair!

How would you like it?
How would you care?
If someone came up
In your room with no care.

Mum, that's not fair!

I haven't forgotten that broken chair,
Right now I should be pulling your hair.

Mum, that's not fair!

Touch your things,
Sit on your bed,
Fall asleep,
You would turn red.

Mum, that's not fair!

**Cienda Soares (11)**
**Our Lady Of Lourdes RC Primary School, Leigh-On-Sea**


# Milo

He is very fluffy
He is very cool
He always falls
He takes me to school.

I am very happy
I am very cool
I always trip
When I go to school.

**Chloe Perrotton (11)**
**Our Lady Of Lourdes RC Primary School, Leigh-On-Sea**

## On The Battleground

Being a soldier you get to look bolder
And fight for your country too.
But there can be bad luck of a bullet going pluck
And you dropping dead on the floor.

A plane soaring through the sky,
Like a bird in mid-flight,
The enemy suddenly comes in sight.
Some machine-gun fire and your light goes dim,
Then you realise your death is grim.

In a tank the tracks go clank,
Then there is a ka-boom,
All of a sudden there is a zoom,
Then you know you've met your doom.

**Robert Alani (11)**
**Our Lady Of Lourdes RC Primary School, Leigh-On-Sea**


## Books

Some books are big
Some books are small
Some books have loads of words
Some none at all
Some people love books
Some people don't
Some people read them
Some people won't
No one realises books are full of surprises
Some have sunsets
Some have sunrises
Some books you have nothing to think about
Some books make you want to shout
Some books also make you cry
And some books even tell a lie.

**Natasha Jaywant (9)**
**Our Lady Of Lourdes RC Primary School, Leigh-On-Sea**

# The Beautiful Game

Football resembles a complicated dance.
All the players begin to prance,
In different directions but all knowing,
Exactly where they should be going.
As the goal is in Arsenal's sight,
The fans shout in sheer delight.
The ball goes flying in the net,
That's a goal they'll never forget.
Tottenham Hotspur still stand proud,
Not to disappoint the crowd.
They continue with their dance,
While they've still got one more chance.
The crowd is stunned, they stand with awe,
As Tottenham begin to score.
The whistle blows, it's a draw, one-all,
Robbie Keane takes home the match ball.
The seats are now empty at White Hart Lane,
As Pele said, 'It's the beautiful game.'

**Katharine Nutman  (11)**
**Our Lady Of Lourdes RC Primary School, Leigh-On-Sea**


# Home

Home is a place where love reaches four walls
A place where happiness never falls
Home is a peacemaker, a dream come true
A rainbow of joy created for you
Where people are bonded together like bricks
And where love and war do not mix.

Home is a security guard in a way
It looks after you night and day
So when your dreams go pear-shaped and curled
Remember your home is a warm shoulder in a cold world.

**Grace Revill  (11)**
**Our Lady Of Lourdes RC Primary School, Leigh-On-Sea**

# Shadows

Can you feel the shadows?
Can you see the light?
Can you hear the whispers in the dark of night?

The trees all shake
I'm so scared
From this dream I hope to awake.

'Let me out,'
But though I try
No one can hear me shout.

Can you feel the shadows?
Can you see the light?
Can you hear the whispers in the dark of night?

Vampire bats
I see in my head
Woodcutters chopping with a razor-sharp axe.

I think of home
My nice, warm bed
I've never felt so alone.

Can you feel the shadows?
Can you see the light?
Can you hear the whispers in the dark of night?

Monsters I know
Just aren't real
Someone's behind me
*Oh no!*

I start to turn
I fall to the ground
This has only just begun.

Can you feel the shadows?
Can you see the light?
Can you hear the whispers in the dark of night?

Someone warm
Is holding me
Cradling my dress, ragged and torn.

Home we go
It's mum
Now I know.

Can you feel the shadows?
Can you see the light?
Can you hear the whispers in the dark of night?

**Megan Calladine  (11)**
**Our Lady Of Lourdes RC Primary School, Leigh-On-Sea**


# War Is Wrong

Shrieking calls,
People crying,
Bombs exploding,
People dying.

Houses in ruins,
Planes in the sky,
Flames everywhere,
War is a fright.

The siren goes off,
Run underground,
Watching and waiting,
As they bomb out the town.

Why don't they talk instead of using the gun,
Killing people just for fun?
Too much fighting,
Where is the peace?

*War is wrong!*

**Lewis Jackson  (11)**
**Our Lady Of Lourdes RC Primary School, Leigh-On-Sea**

# In The Eyes Of The Sun

Rising slowly above the hills,
Looking out at the lakes and windmills,
As he lets out beautiful sun rays,
I look up at the yellow blaze.
The sky is glowing
And the clouds drift,
The wind blows quietly,
Calm and swift.
Flowers sway to and fro,
While all around them green grass grows.
Looking at the people in the town,
Hoping that he will not see a frown
Because of such a beautiful day
Some people go to the beach and play.
The sun's light rests on glistening water,
As it dazzles every son and daughter.
The night has come
But today was fun.
This was a day in the eyes of the sun
And now I will say -
Goodnight, everyone.

**Erin Blowers  (10)**
**Our Lady Of Lourdes RC Primary School, Leigh-On-Sea**


# My Friend The Rat

I had a little friend who was a rat
Who lived in a cupboard in the house
He was very frightened of the cat
But did not mind the little mouse.

His name was Fred and his colour black
But he was chased by rat catcher Jack
He said he'd cook him for his roast
But Fred laughed and said, 'Don't boast!'

**Paul Flynn  (10)**
**Our Lady Of Lourdes RC Primary School, Leigh-On-Sea**

# The Effect Of War

People dying, people crying, that is the effect of war,
The effect of war is like a saw, cutting everything down
And leaving nothing in its wake.
Everything gone, everything bare
Like a bear being shorn of its hair
This is the effect of war.
Everything is barren, everything is gone
And you can hear the mournful song of the trees,
They are gone forever,
Never to be seen.
They never should have been
But they were
And they have disappeared
Off the face of the Earth.
This is the effect of *war!*

**Charles Innocent (10)**
**Our Lady Of Lourdes RC Primary School, Leigh-On-Sea**


# Anne Frank

What's the reason for this treason?
I'm burning in this, burning for the worse.
I'm going to burst as I curse when a hearse goes by.
I'm trapped in my four-wall prison.
All I can do is bounce my ball across the wall as the days pass by.
Why should we die?
Is it one big lie?
All I can do is sigh.
I'm caught in the quarrel of the mighty sides,
All I can do is hide from their massive tide.
I'm blind to their mighty blast that traps you just too fast.

**Jacob Cox (11)**
**Our Lady Of Lourdes RC Primary School, Leigh-On-Sea**

# Horses' Hilarious Seasons

Horses love summer, there's so much to eat,
They jump up so high and spring off their feet.
Gallop, gallop, gallop away into the stable, lie down on the hay.

Wake up, wake up, snow is falling,
Wrap up warm, it's winter's morning.
It's getting too cold, time for bed,
Lie down on the straw and rest your head.

Wake up, wake up, there's leaves all around,
We shall run, run as fast as we can
With the leaves at our feet and the wind in our mane,
Faster and faster our hooves will go
Into the stable one more time,
Make sure you're comfy and have a long snooze.

Wake up, wake up, spring has come,
Let's play and play under the sun.
Yippee! One by one we shall go to bed
And see what lies in store for us tomorrow.

**Sydney Stevenson (9)**
**Our Lady Of Lourdes RC Primary School, Leigh-On-Sea**


# Summer

Boiling hot is the yellow sand
I have to sit, I cannot stand
The bright rays of the sun are burning me
It even stings when I go in the sea
It is at least 60 degrees
I can't stand this heat
I must have a breeze
I go inside
It is a lot colder
I look at my burns
I feel I'm getting older.

**Madeleine Newton (10)**
**Our Lady Of Lourdes RC Primary School, Leigh-On-Sea**

# Summer

Summer is my favourite season
I can watch the flowers for hours
I hear the birds humming
So I know they're coming
The trees are growing taller
With the shadows making it cooler.

Every year I wait, I hate it
I wait for summer to come again.

In the summer children play
Away in the park
Even when it's dark
All day long I bathe in the sun
And have fun.

Now summer's gone, moving along
For the next season to come
No more fun, no sun
Back to school again.

**Kate Hayden  (10)**
**Our Lady Of Lourdes RC Primary School, Leigh-On-Sea**


# Why?

I'm not sure why I wanted to fly,
It made me die and that's no lie.

The plane crashed and I was trashed
And that's how I died and was put aside.

I was only a young lad, I must have gone mad
To fly and think I wouldn't die.

Now I'm dead with no head,
Why did I want to fly? For now I am dead!

**Jack Farrell  (10)**
**Our Lady Of Lourdes RC Primary School, Leigh-On-Sea**

## As The Grave Bows Down

Owen, oh Owen, he calls,
They're coming over, over, over,
The lines march down before them,
Fear strikes into their eyes.

Owen, oh Owen, he calls,
They're here, they're here, they're here,
Don't bow down before them,
Shoot away, away, away.

Owen, oh Owen, he calls,
They're in, they're in, they're in,
Gunshots poured in front of them,
With blood gushing here and there.

Owen, oh Owen, he would have called,
If the gun had only paused,
Coffins have taken him away,
To a land with no breath.

**Matthew Sessions (10)**
**Our Lady Of Lourdes RC Primary School, Leigh-On-Sea**


## Monster Lary

There's a monster called Lary
He really is that scary
He's very, very smelly
And has a fat belly
There's a wart on his nose
And spots on his toes
He has three bulging eyes
That's why people say their goodbyes!
And never come to the woods again!

**Christine Harris (8)**
**Our Lady Of Lourdes RC Primary School, Leigh-On-Sea**

# I Would Hate . . .

I would hate . . .
To get sent to my room
To get hit by a broom
To be in a country of doom
To get locked in a tomb.

I would hate . . .
To get hit in the face
For someone to lay an ace
To trip over my lace
To lose a race by running at a too-slow pace.

I would hate . . .
To break my back
To get put in a sack
To lose my friend Jack
To get a big whack.

But sometimes things like that happen!

**Ryan Fawcett (9)**
**Our Lady Of Lourdes RC Primary School, Leigh-On-Sea**

# Guns

Firing guns are deadly tools,
Firing rifles and German pistols,
Shooting the bullet right through the air,
Trying to shoot the small, brown hare.

Shooting our target, it falls to the ground,
We run up to it to see what we've found,
Looking in the bush to see what was there
And to our surprise it's the hare.

We run back home and tell our mum,
That we've shot a hare in the bum,
We run back over to the green bush
But the hare is no longer there.

**Dominic Craik (10)**
**Our Lady Of Lourdes RC Primary School, Leigh-On-Sea**

# My Food Dream

I dream of a delicious fruit and fudge fantasy,
especially made from my home Leigh.

I dream of a slippery sensation,
giving to me by the holy nation.
I dream of a pleasured pork,
wondrously made in New York.

I dream of a fabulous fried fish,
served in a most beautiful dish.
I dream of a bowl of roasted rice,
incredibly lovely and very nice.

I dream of a heavenly ham,
given to me by my friend Sam.
I dream of supreme spaghetti,
made for me on a jetty.

I dream of chunky chips,
ludicrously tasty for my lips.
I dream of delicious doughnuts,
very tasty with a few nuts.

That is my food dream,
I hope it made you gleam.

**Luke McGeoch (10)**
**Our Lady Of Lourdes RC Primary School, Leigh-On-Sea**

# Beautiful Beastly Beasts

Frogs, newts and salamanders,
monitors, lizards and snakes,
budgies, crows and butterflies
and other things that shake.

Kangaroos jump up high,
flying squirrels almost fly,
slimy worms like to squiggle,
puppy dogs like to wriggle.

Chimps like eating juicy fruits,
snails love eating flowers' shoots,
lions gobble up hopping gazelles,
thrushes eat snails in shells.

Chameleons hide by camouflage,
elephants can hide even when very large,
crocodiles hide beneath the green,
so they cannot be seen.

All these beautiful beastly beasts,
enjoy their weird and wonderful feasts
but the weirdest of them all
is the human animal!

**Eleanor Mitchelmore (10)**
**Our Lady Of Lourdes RC Primary School, Leigh-On-Sea**

# Snowball Fight

I jumped out of bed,
raring to go,
all I could think of was the snow
and how white and cold it is.

I ran downstairs to put on my boots
and rushed towards the garden gate.

I joined my friends
who were waiting for me
and off we went to go and see
a battlefield full of wounded boys,
covered in layers of thick clothes.

We were eager to join this fearsome fight
and built some army barracks.

The sun went down at quarter to six,
we played as time ticks,
we were winning
and I hit six,
time ticked on and then a sudden chill
down my spine
and a massive wood pine
stood there in line,
we all knew it was time to go
and we hope tomorrow there will be
*snow!*

**Oliver Hart  (10)**
**Our Lady Of Lourdes RC Primary School, Leigh-On-Sea**

# School Days

Waiting on the playground,
Standing in my line,
Luckily today's not bad,
The weather has been fine.

Noisy classroom, teacher shouts!
Chairs are scraping, children pout,
Scurrying to settle down,
Teacher standing with a frown.

Finally the work begins,
Quietly we write,
If we finish silently,
Extra play, we might?

Practising for Borough Sports,
Running really fast,
Saying silent prayers,
'Please don't make me last!'

Now it's time for singing,
Practising our play,
Will we concentrate and listen,
Learning well today.

During lunch, lots of chatter
Enjoying time with my friends,
Hoping lunch lasts much longer,
Playtime never ends.

In the classroom we prepare,
For helping our new readers,
Little ones who have just begun,
We will be their leaders.

Taking care of others,
This has been my goal,
I hope Year 6 will never end
Happiness locked within my soul.

**Lucy Haswell (11)**
**Our Lady Of Lourdes RC Primary School, Leigh-On-Sea**

# Shopping

Going shopping is always great fun,
Cos we go to the café for a drink and a bun!

Clothes in the window, shoes on display,
There's a half-price sale during the month of May!

In shop no1 I look at earrings,
Then I jump as the counter bell rings!

Clothes in the window, shoes on display,
There's a half-price sale during the month of May!

In shop no2 there's some boots that are nice
And they're at a reasonable price!

Clothes in the window, shoes on display,
There's a half-price sale during the month of May!

Now I'm in the penultimate shop
And I come back out with a glittery top!

Clothes in the window, shoes on display,
There's a half-price sale during the month of May!

Then from my brother I hear a moan,
'One more shop,' I say (another groan!)

Clothes in the window, shoes on display,
There's a half-price sale during the month of May!

I'm in the last shop and I hear a beep,
It's my mum, 'Take me home - I need some sleep!'

Clothes in the window, shoes on display,
I've had a brilliant, exhausting shopping day!

**Georgina Collingwood (10)**
**Our Lady Of Lourdes RC Primary School, Leigh-On-Sea**

# Leaving School

Scotland's at a loss
For Essex got the boss
You will not slack
With Mrs Mac
Or good old Mr Love.

If I had a choice
I'd stay to hear her voice
She's so sweet
The classroom's neat
We've stacked up all our seats.

At 3 o'clock the bell will ring
I don't know what to do
When I'm older and look back
I will always think of you.

**Michael Arnold  (11)**
**Our Lady Of Lourdes RC Primary School, Leigh-On-Sea**


# Big Bad Giant

Big bad giant
Stomping everywhere
Big bad giant
Looking for someone to scare
Big bad giant
Very, very brave
Big bad giant
Lives inside a cave
Big bad giant
Fell into the sea
Big bad giant
Has hurt his knee
Big bad giant
Walking to Rome
Big bad giant
That's where you will find his home.

**Isobel Mary Hine  (8)**
**Our Lady Of Lourdes RC Primary School, Leigh-On-Sea**

# Monstrous Pets

A venomous snake
A whale, a lake
A dog that only goes woof.

A big, grizzly bear
A snail, a hare
Or a peacock with lots of feathers.

A flying old bird
A hedgehog, a herd
Or a stupid, fat cat on a mat.

A small, little mouse
A dog in a house
Foxes with lots of cubs.

A lying-down rabbit
With a bad habit
Eating lots of carrots.

A fish in a bowl
A mole in a hole
And a horse eating some hay.

A rat in a hat
A yellow bat
And a zebra with lots of stripes.

So some pets are tall
Some pets are small
But a teacher's pet is totally different!

**Alfie Sadowski (11)**
**Our Lady Of Lourdes RC Primary School, Leigh-On-Sea**

# Dogs

Some dogs are small,
Some dogs are tall,
Some dogs are hairy,
Some dogs are scary.
Some dogs run around,
Some just lie around,
Some dogs are lazy
Others are just crazy!

Some dogs have bad habits,
Some dogs chase rabbits,
Some dogs have lots of hair,
Some dogs are bare.
Some dogs are white,
Others are alright.

**Michael Lehane (10)**
**Our Lady Of Lourdes RC Primary School, Leigh-On-Sea**


# Hamster

Small and fast
It skips the past
Ready for action
It causes attraction
It will be your furry friend
Although it will come to an end.

At cage bars he always gnaws
And food he absolutely adores
It always has a cheesy smile
And keeps time flying by
All the time.

**Lewis Irvine (11)**
**Our Lady Of Lourdes RC Primary School, Leigh-On-Sea**

# An Unforgettable Holiday!

It all started one cold day,
When my dad thought we should go away,
I ran upstairs and started to pack,
I threw in some clothes and grabbed a snack.
I ran to the car and opened the door,
Jumped onto the seat and threw my bag on the floor.
When we got there I shouted in glee
And stared down at the sparkling sea.
I ran to the hotel and dived into the pool,
Thinking how great it was to be out of school.
My brother ran to the room and gazed at the bed,
Then jumped onto it banging his head.
I charged out of the pool slipping on the floor,
Breaking my legs and much, much more.
I will always remember this strange holiday,
Every time my dad says we should go away!

**Caroline Packer  (11)**
**Our Lady Of Lourdes RC Primary School, Leigh-On-Sea**


# My Little Brother

Two brown eyes, that sparkle with mischief,
A putty-flat nose and a cheeky grin,
Spiky hair that looks like a hedgehog,

That's my little brother . . .

Two sticky hands and a dirty face,
Podgy, fat legs and two small feet,
Ten tiny toes and a fiery temper,

That's my little brother . . .

Big, lovely cuddles and slobbery kisses,
Loads of hits and a few near-misses,
Plenty of energy and tons of love,

That's my little brother . . .

**Daniel Smith  (10)**
**Our Lady Of Lourdes RC Primary School, Leigh-On-Sea**

# Football's Coming Home!

Football, football, so much fun
Sometimes scoring in the sun,
Scoring goals makes you feel good,
I would play all day if I could.

Celebrating with your team
Is something that we all would dream.
They shout and scream with lots of joy
As they announce the goal on the tannoy.

After the whistle blows for half-time,
We go in the changing rooms to have some lime.
We have to cool before we walk on the pitch,
Some players are large, some players are titch.

Some of the players are nervous and scared
As they walk on with their shirts all teared.

The ball is very bouncy in this match,
The ball is also very attached.

As they all walked off clapping their hands
And the other team are going mad.

**Amy Nash  (11)**
**Our Lady Of Lourdes RC Primary School, Leigh-On-Sea**

# Within Their Spirits

Within their spirits,
That lie beneath,
Lie truth, darkness and belief
And when that darkness takes control,
All that's left is an empty hole,
Small and dark is the hole,
Just like the love that lies below
And when that faithful man comes along,
He will release them with this song.

**Thomas Young  (11)**
**Our Lady Of Lourdes RC Primary School, Leigh-On-Sea**

# Leaving School

I'm leaving school
Hip, hip, hooray!
It's the end of the year
And we start the holiday!

I pack my books
And say goodbye
I walk out the gates
And my fans start to cry.

I pick up my bag
And get in the car
My mum starts driving
Far and far.

I'm very happy
But also sad
For all the wonderful
Times I had.

I'm leaving school
Hip, hip, hooray!
It's the end of the year
And we start the holiday!

**Daisy Asaman  (11)**
**Our Lady Of Lourdes RC Primary School, Leigh-On-Sea**

# The Forest

The wind flies through my fingers
The trees scream in my ear,
I'm snuggling up in a cave
And I'm shivering with fear.

My family have all left me
I don't know where they are
They're probably at home all warm
Or driving in their car.

They probably haven't realised
That I'm left here all alone
I bet they don't care
That I want to come home.

This forest is really spooky
I've been here for about one week.
I just wish they loved me
It's so cold I cannot sleep.

As the trees grow bigger and bigger
I'm scared and stuck here all alone.
I feel I'm going to die so soon
Oh why won't they let me home?

**Natasha Everall (11)**
**Our Lady Of Lourdes RC Primary School, Leigh-On-Sea**

# Saying Goodbye!

I am now leaving the school
Going to miss the teachers
Down by the pond I wave
To all the creatures.

Now all trees are waving to us
Or is it just the wind?
There's no need to make a fuss.

English, maths and history are not
As good as music and PE.

I am leaving for another school
Saying goodbye to friends and all.
Everyone is very sad
But if they're not they must be mad.

But sorry, Mrs Mac, going to have to say goodbye,
I'm going to miss the school,
I promise I won't *cry!*

**Joss Chandler (11)**
**Our Lady Of Lourdes RC Primary School, Leigh-On-Sea**

# Last Day Of School

It's the last day of school tomorrow.
It's everybody's dream.
Waiting for the bell to ring.
It's everybody's dream.
Out they run with screams and shouts
For a wonderful dream.

**Dylan O'Regan (11)**
**Our Lady Of Lourdes RC Primary School, Leigh-On-Sea**

# Is It The End Of Our Friends?

Is it the end of our friends?
Will we see them ever again?
Some at school, some at home
Some in the sunlight or some in the dark.

Maybe I'm right, maybe I'm wrong
Whatever happens it will be done
I started in reception, that was fun
Now we're leaving with a tear in our eyes.

It's gone so fast, like a leopard zooming
Through a mighty jungle
If I could restart time
We would be in reception again.

If senior school is as good as this
You might as well make the most of it!

**Thomas Hannaway (10)**
**Our Lady Of Lourdes RC Primary School, Leigh-On-Sea**


# The End Of Year 6 Already

The day has come for me to go,
I'm feeling rather sad.
My teachers have been brilliant
And some are rather mad.
My mum's in the kitchen,
Cooking our school lunch.
The kids line up with their trays,
They are a cool bunch.
The end of year production is 'Under The Sea'.
We'll try and do our best, so please come and see.
I'll start at St Bernard's this September
And wow! What an adventure it'll be.

**Jessica Peters (11)**
**Our Lady Of Lourdes RC Primary School, Leigh-On-Sea**

# When The Lion Got Out Of The Zoo!

There once was a lion called Prowl,
She pranced through the zoo with a growl.
She ate up a bunch of boys for her lunch
In a terrible way that was foul.

Now this lion she caused a great stir
But because of her camouflaged fur
She couldn't be found
Above or underground
So they said there's no point looking for her.

Now young Prowl was out of the zoo
She caused a big hullabaloo.
The townsfolk were frightened
As the great tension tightened
And make a big fuss, it is true.

Now Prowl had made them all worry,
So they thought of plan in a hurry
To catch the big lion
They sent out old Ryan
To just end this enormous flurry.

**Mary-Ellen Lewis  (9)**
**Our Lady Of Lourdes RC Primary School, Leigh-On-Sea**


# If Only

If only, if only the moon speaks no reply
The sun that shines as it goes by.
Be strong, my wolf, turn around boldly.
Fly high, my baby bird
My angel, my only.

**Natalie Oliffe  (9)**
**Our Lady Of Lourdes RC Primary School, Leigh-On-Sea**

# My Family

My family are with me every day
And my brother has gone away
He has gone to a flat with his girlfriend
She's going to have a baby, it might be a boy
I hope it is because girls are so annoying.

Girls are expensive
Girls are not needed
Girls are boring.

I hope it's a boy
I hope he's good at football
I hope he has my smile
I hope he's like me.

**James Watson (11)**
**Our Lady Of Lourdes RC Primary School, Leigh-On-Sea**


# Gymnastics

I can do handstands,
You can do cartwheels,
I can do cartwheels
And you can do handstands.
I can do jumps,
You can do leaps,
I can do leaps
And you can do jumps.
I can do backflips,
You can do gymnastics,
I can do gymnastics,
You can do backflips.
    Yeah!

**Rebecca Rangue (10)**
**Our Lady Of Lourdes RC Primary School, Leigh-On-Sea**

# Art

Art is excellent fun
But majorly messy.
You can copy a huge bowl
Of juicy fruit.
You can trace an evil -
Looking devil with fangs.
You can make things out of
Cardboard and tissue paper.
You can do anything.
You can paint a waterfall
By the mountains.
You can draw a rainbow
With a river.
You can colour a garden
With lots of flowers.
Have a fantastic fun time.
Wear an apron if you have one.
I love art so much,
So why don't you love it with me?

**Gemma Sears  (10)**
**Our Lady Of Lourdes RC Primary School, Leigh-On-Sea**


# Mr Smee

There was a little man called Mr Smee,
he ran round the garden like a little flea.

He had a little goose, nothing would it wear
except a little feather and the rest of the goose was bare.

That little man called Mr Smee,
he ran round the gardenlike a little flea.

He had a little cat, nothing could it do
except sit on a mat cos it was too fat!

And that's the end of that!

**Elizabeth Leftley  (8)**
**Our Lady Of Lourdes RC Primary School, Leigh-On-Sea**

# Buttons

Buttons is my kitten
She's only ten weeks old
Her fur is blackish-brown
And her eyes are glistening gold.

Her teeth and claws are as sharp as pins
Her tongue as rough as sand
But she still is very tiny
And fits into my hands.

Buttons likes to play
With anything at all
But her very favourite toy
Is her stripy rainbow ball.

She tires really quickly
She'll often need a nap
Her favourite place to sleep
Is curled up on my lap.

Once she jumped into the bath
She got extremely wet
Her ears go back and sometimes
I think she gets upset.

When she has her milk
It goes all over her
I know she loves her milk though
I can hear her gentle purr.

At night she has her mad time
Normally round about eight
Climbing up and down our plants
Which now are in a state.

I love my kitten Buttons
She means the world to me
I think she means the same
To my loving family.

**Hannah Murray (9)**
**Our Lady Of Lourdes RC Primary School, Leigh-On-Sea**

# My Guinea Pigs

My guinea pigs are crazy,
They are very greedy too.
My guinea pigs are crazy
But I love them still, it's true.

Their names are Heidi and Daisy.
One's smooth and one is rough.
They love to munch on grass all day,
In fact, they just can't get enough!

They like to make a funny noise,
You could call it quite a squeak
And in the mornings when I put them out
This squeak is at its peak!

They only seem to make this noise
When they know that I am near.
That's how I know that my little pigs
Think I am very dear.

I really love my guinea pigs,
I know them really well.
I really love my guinea pigs,
As I'm sure that you can tell.

**Mollie Westmore  (10)**
**Our Lady Of Lourdes RC Primary School, Leigh-On-Sea**

# Shapes

S hapes, semi-circle, sphere
H exagon, hemisphere, hexagon
A ngle,
P rism, pyramid, pentagon
E quilateral triangle
S quare, shape, sphere.

**James Hudson  (8)**
**Our Lady Of Lourdes RC Primary School, Leigh-On-Sea**

# My Pets

Some pets are slow like the snails that live in a tank upstairs.
Others are fast like the rabbits when they run loose in the garden.
My fish are slippery, shiny and gold
and have scales instead of hairs
But they all have bad manners and push by
without even saying pardon.

The guinea pigs, Muffin and Gizmo, are squeaky, soft,
hairy and small.
Pippin the hamster is curious, bright, fun and healthy.
The water snails are cleaners of the home that the fish live in
in the hall.
Dad said, 'If we didn't have all these creatures
we would be quite wealthy.'

My cat Jessie is fluffy, soft and playful with very sharp claws.
The pond in the garden is wild and home to frogs and a newt.
Bruno my dog likes long walks and has lots of toys
that he leaves on the floors.
Mum gets fed up with clearing all the mess
but admits that they are really quite cute.

**Alexandra Allen (10)**
**Our Lady Of Lourdes RC Primary School, Leigh-On-Sea**


# A Lick Off A Spoon

Ice cream or cake,
What can you make?
Cherry pie, are you sly?
A lick of a spoon from the moon.
Cake
Ice cream
Pie
All used with a spoon from the moon.

**Evan Stobart (8)**
**Our Lady Of Lourdes RC Primary School, Leigh-On-Sea**

# Football Madness

Referee
Can't you see
That player is hacking me?

He came in quick
And had a miss-kick
Isn't that a free kick?

Liam, you take
Don't make a mistake
Then when it comes to you, Gavin, pretend to fake.

Handball!
Not at all
It's the ref's decision after all.

Penalty!
Referee, didn't you see
He has just collided with me?

Come on, Dave
Don't misbehave
Just make this save.

At the end of the game
We were not ashamed
Because we won the title and will win it again.

**Gavin Bull  (9)**
**Our Lady Of Lourdes RC Primary School, Leigh-On-Sea**


# Poetry

P oetry is different,
O h, I mean weird,
E lephants trump if they hear the sound,
T all and skinny,
R are and unlucky,
Y ou are like that sometimes.

**Rebecca Bertram  (8)**
**Our Lady Of Lourdes RC Primary School, Leigh-On-Sea**

# Infinity

'The sky's the limit' -
That's what they say;
The moon, the stars -
Can I make it all the way?
Not me, not I - no, surely not.
Is there a chance I can do it?
I'll give it all I've got.

Run faster, aim higher, striving all the way;
I know I can do it, this is going to be my day.
I can feel it in my bones, a tingle in my toes;
I'm holding back, running in, letting it all go.
It's all going to happen if I keep my cool;
I'm almost there, just one more push.
I'm giving it my all.

Wow! That feels wonderful -
I've reached the sky and more!
My breath is gone, my heart beats fast;
I've opened up the door!
Is the sky the limit?
Is that what they say?
No, I don't think so - I'm going all the way.

**Isabelle Claire Morgan (10)**
**Our Lady Of Lourdes RC Primary School, Leigh-On-Sea**

# Conor

C onor is crazy, he's
O n the roof
N aughty me
O opsy daisy! I fell off the
R oof!

**Conor O'Hart (8)**
**Our Lady Of Lourdes RC Primary School, Leigh-On-Sea**

# There's A Cat Stuck In My Tree

There's a cat stuck in my tree
And I don't know what to do,
There's a cat stuck in my tree
And that's why I am asking you.

Should I call the firefighters?
Or maybe it's not so bad,
Should I climb up a ladder?
Oh, that cat looks mad.

So mum has called the firefighters,
They can save the poor cat,
So I can go and play,
Oh, that cat's got my hat!

**Rebecca Ravinet (9)**
**Our Lady Of Lourdes RC Primary School, Leigh-On-Sea**


# England's Euro 2004

On Portugal's ground the players run
Scoring goals and having fun
The year we play is 2004
Hope Beckham and Owen score.

Hope to see good players there
Doing tricks with lots of flare
Sven's the one to see us through
With Beckham and his football crew.

He's number 7
With his feet from Heaven
Rooney too
He'll score a few.

With cheers from all around
We'll dribble the ball along the ground
I hope that England win a prize
And aren't knocked out with sad goodbyes.

**Liam King (10)**
**Our Lady Of Lourdes RC Primary School, Leigh-On-Sea**

## Soccer Stars

There once was a footballer called Joe Cole,
Who stuck his head down a hole,
His head got hit by a pole,
Then he saw a gigantic mole.

He passed the ball to Adrian Mutu,
Who said he loved Pokemon and Mewtwo,
He looked at a train and said, 'Choo-choo,'
He also watches the Teletubbies with Noo-Noo.

He booted the ball to Gary Neville,
Who didn't know how to throw a pebble,
He got in the box,
Scored a goal!

The crowd went wild,
Although the weather was very mild,
They all went home drinking beer
But the price was really dear.

**Liam Glynn  (9)**
**Our Lady Of Lourdes RC Primary School, Leigh-On-Sea**

## An Old Firm Game

There was an old firm game
Between Southend and Blackpool.
It was pretty lame
Because the managers sat on a stool.

You could get really bored
To watch Blackpool play
But then Southend scored
Because the keeper stood like clay.

Southend ended up winning
1-0 was the score.
The Southend team were grinning
To hear the crowd roar.

**Connor Stewart  (10)**
**Our Lady Of Lourdes RC Primary School, Leigh-On-Sea**

# Every Day

Every day
I listen to the radio
I watch TV
I sometimes read the newspapers
But I find it hard to put in words what I can see.

Mothers crying
People dying
Bodies torn limb from limb
Another bomb has gone off today
I cannot believe what is happening.

They say the war is over
It doesn't look like it to me
The politicians say everything is fine
And peace will come eventually
Why don't they tell the truth?

I wish I could understand
But I am only a child
All I want is peace and happiness wherever it may be
I pray to God that one day
That is what I will see.

**Sophie Logue (10)**
**Our Lady Of Lourdes RC Primary School, Leigh-On-Sea**

# Cluck-Cluck Black Sheep
*(Inspired by 'Baa Baa Black Sheep')*

Cluck-cluck black sheep
Have you any milk?
Yes, sir, yes, sir, three eggs full
One for the go-kart,
One for the crane,
One for the little boy
Who lives down the drain.

**Henry Smith (9)**
**Our Lady Of Lourdes RC Primary School, Leigh-On-Sea**

# Daytime

In the daytime when the bees are buzzing
And the rabbits are quickly running,
The fluffy, white clouds above you
Are moving very slowly and the owls aren't going 'Hoot.'

My dog is wildly barking
Trying to chase a cat that is just staring
At my fish that are smoothly swimming
In their home on our pond.

When the sun is beaming
And the moon is not shining,
The sun makes me feel nice and warm
Knowing that there won't be a storm.

As I lay on my back
Looking up at the sky without a lack
Of blue sky, the silky grass is brushing against me
Taking in all that I can see.

What a wonderful daytime in our fabulous world.

**Gerard D Huggins (10)**
**Our Lady Of Lourdes RC Primary School, Leigh-On-Sea**


# Poetry Themes

The happiest sound in the world
must be my mum smiling at me.

The loveliest sound in the world
must be a baby looking at me.

The nicest sound in the world
must be a boy eating chocolate with me.

The quietest sound in the world
must be a mouse with me.

**Sofia Valente (8)**
**Our Lady Of Lourdes RC Primary School, Leigh-On-Sea**

# The Seaside Mermaid

Tropical fish weaving around each other
Glittering the colours of the rainbow,
The sea is clear as a diamond glistening
As far as the eye can see,
Waves snaking like dolphins.

The sun is like a bright yellow ball with sparkling rays
Of glorious sunlight and streaks like yellow highlights.

The sky as blue as a sapphire,
Stretched over to the horizon,
The sky reflecting in the clear sea,
No clouds to be seen floating in the water.

The soft sand grains as white as a dove's feathers,
It stretches for miles upon miles
And the soft sand grains as soft as silk.

The fresh, sea air,
The fishy smell,
No wonder I love *my* home!

**Zoë Rusz  (10)**
**Our Lady Of Lourdes RC Primary School, Leigh-On-Sea**


# Changing

Light to dark
Wire to machine
Page to book
Sand to glass
Letter to word
Life to death
We all change.

**Dexter Bardua  (9)**
**Our Lady Of Lourdes RC Primary School, Leigh-On-Sea**

# In The Still Of The Night

In the still of the night,
When you can hear every sound,
I can hear from outside,
A twig crack on the ground.

In the still of the night,
When I can't see a thing,
The house comes to life
And I can hear everything.

In the still of the night,
When I can hear a mouse squeak,
I hear heavy footsteps,
Then the door starts to creak.

In the still of the night,
Something tugs at my hair,
I turn round to see,
That there's a man standing there.

He bends over slightly,
I can smell his bad breath,
He raises his dagger
And stabs me to death.

I take my last breath
And let out a scream,
I wake with a thud,
It's only a dream!

**Daniel Kidney (10)**
**Our Lady Of Lourdes RC Primary School, Leigh-On-Sea**

# Socks

Smelly socks
Heart socks
Blue socks
Banana socks
Flower socks
Green socks
Santa socks
Queen socks
black socks
Socks, socks, socks, socks
Any
kind
of
socks
you
can
think
of.

**Isabelle Dex (9)**
**Our Lady Of Lourdes RC Primary School, Leigh-On-Sea**


# Spring

The wondrous world whizzes past,
The waters will always last.
The lemon, lazy sun lazes
As the cool winds watch the clouds run.
The bees buzz and that's because the flowers are blooming.
The colours are booming.
The grass sways, the trees have their own ways
And that is how I describe spring.

**Morgan Power (9)**
**Our Lady Of Lourdes RC Primary School, Leigh-On-Sea**

# Weather

Weather, oh, weather
What could it be?
A gale, a thunderstorm?
Don't ask me!
If it's pouring
It will be boring
Don't ask me!
Maybe it's crashing, smashing
Or bashing
Don't ask me!
Thunderstorms yelling
Lightning swelling high
Up in the sky
Don't ask me!
But whatever the weather
It's got to be fun.
Don't ask me!

**Phoebe Sleigh-Johnson  (9)**
**Our Lady Of Lourdes RC Primary School, Leigh-On-Sea**


# Dad, You Are Not Funny

Dad, you are not funny,
You'll never make me laugh,
You're really embarrassing,
Everyone thinks you're daft.

Dad, you will not make me laugh,
You can stand and wait for ever,
You can tickle, tickle me all you like,
You can even use a feather.

So do you get the picture?
You'll never make me laugh,
You really are embarrassing
And everyone thinks you're daft.

**Michael Haughton & Joseph Collingwood  (9)**
**Our Lady Of Lourdes RC Primary School, Leigh-On-Sea**

# Poetry Fun

The smallest sound in the world
must be an ant crawling on me.

The funniest sight in the world
must be a crown hanging from a tree.

The silliest sight in the world
must be my dad crying to me.

The loudest sound in the world
must be a drum banging for me.

The scariest sound in the world
must be a wolf growling at me.

**Bradley Seaden  (8)**
**Our Lady Of Lourdes RC Primary School, Leigh-On-Sea**


# Nonsense Poem!

Big bad dwarf
small as you can be,
watch out, he's still
very clever he can
climb tall trees!

Watch out around
you, look down below
I'm sure he'll come
up to you and bite
off your toe!

So if you don't watch
out you'll need your
voice to shout!
For the big bad dwarf
is always standing
there, ready to scare!

**Rosie Revill  (8)**
**Our Lady Of Lourdes RC Primary School, Leigh-On-Sea**

# My Favourite Food

Chocolate, crisps, toffees, sweets, cakes
and doughnuts can be beat!
Ice cream is my favourite treat with lots and lots of pie to eat!

Spaghetti, pasta, ketchup, cheese,
mix them together makes a pasta breeze!
White bread, egg mayonnaise, dot of ham, what a lovely day!

When I eat all that lovely food
I chew and chomp and chew, chew, chew!

**Joseph Heath  (8)**
**Our Lady Of Lourdes RC Primary School, Leigh-On-Sea**


# The Animals' Song

The animals of the billabong
Like to have a singasong
Now every now and then
I take a stroll through the outback
And one particular day on my little stroll
I heard a little song
Coming from that billabong and this is how it went:

'Oh, the Monitas a ringing and the dingo is a dinging
so it's about time we got moving
on our yearly sing-a-song.
We all live in this billabong.
Frog, cobra then the croc that's a bit of the food chain.
The Thorny Devil hides among the leaves
Only to emerge to have one little sing-a-song!
We'd like to dedicate our song to everything we've eaten.'

So if you're taking a stroll in the outback
And hear that little song
You know you're near that billabong.

**Shaun Gendall  (10)**
**Our Lady Of Lourdes RC Primary School, Leigh-On-Sea**

# The Weird Sea!

A submarine once went down to the weird sea
and what did he *sea?*
but a shark having a cup of tea!
He went down some more
and what did he *sea?*
but a clown fish in a funny seat up in a tree
and another in a banana can!
Two hours later he saw a starfish
getting ready for a blast in space to *sea!*
His cousins!
*What a weird sea!*

**Michael O'Hara  (8)**
**Our Lady Of Lourdes RC Primary School, Leigh-On-Sea**


# Strawberries And Cream

Strawberries and cream
Really makes you want to scream!
Apple pie and custard
Looks like mustard!

Banana split
If I don't get it I'll have a fit!
Knickerbocker glory
Is as exciting as a story!

Chocolate mousse
With sour lemon juice!
Apple tart
Straight to my heart!

Trifle
As good as shooting a rifle!
I love fudge
I mash it into a sludge!

Yummy jelly
For my belly!

**Hannah Matthews  (10)**
**Our Lady Of Lourdes RC Primary School, Leigh-On-Sea**

# I Would Like . . .

To hear the sound of the breeze
To touch the wind on the trees
To swim rivers, seas and oceans
To climb the most humungous mountain.

I would like . . .
To jogtrot around the world
To listen to the wolves howling at the blue moon
To sing a melody with the birds
To fly with the golden eagle.

I would like . . .
To walk every gleaming rainbow
To cha-cha in the falling rain
To go to the shining sun
To shout to the great and noble Queen.

I would like . . .
To swing with all the monkeys
To sleep with all the lions
To laugh with the hyenas
To run with a leopard.

I would like . . .
To hop with a kangaroo
To talk with the great white shark
To speak with blue mermaids
But most of all I would like to cry with all the whales.
Can I?

**Elizabeth Chuck  (10)**
**Our Lady Of Lourdes RC Primary School, Leigh-On-Sea**

# Butterflies

Butterflies fly in the summer breeze,
every wing so dedicated to glide and get them high in the sky.

Every wing so delicate, each is perfectly decorated,
the proboscis mouth to suck the tasty nectar
from every single flower.

It's a fascinating thing.

It starts an ugly thing then blooms
into the most beautiful of all insects.

It's a fascinating thing.

But the last thing it does is lay its eggs
and then dies,
then its work is done.

**Natalie Williams  (10)**
**Our Lady Of Lourdes RC Primary School, Leigh-On-Sea**


# As I Swim Along!

As I swim round and round
My legs go up and down
Backstroke, front crawl, breaststroke too
Swimming's the life
And swimming's what I do.
Now I'm doing the butterfly
And it feels like I can really fly.
My arms go up and my legs go down
But now I can't hear a single sound.
Everyone has left me on my own
To glide by my side.
I swim along the flattened surface
I look left and I look right.
The sun shines through the window,
It's very bright.
Then suddenly everyone jumps in
And splashes me just for spite.

**Lidia Russo  (10)**
**Our Lady Of Lourdes RC Primary School, Leigh-On-Sea**

# Films

Actors love action
Action with adventure
That thrills and entertains.

The media loves gossip
Gossip with snapshots
That flash and annoy.

Actresses love comedy
Comedy with laughs
That's funny and hilarious.

Animators love graphics
Graphics that made manga
Manga with suspense.

Film producers love the Odeon
The Odeon that brings you new films
So sit back, watch and enjoy.

**Sarah Chalkley (10)**
**Our Lady Of Lourdes RC Primary School, Leigh-On-Sea**


# The Jumping Something

The bush rattled,
I went about a foot away,
It moved again!
*What was it?* I asked myself that day.

Amongst the chestnut tree,
It made a slithering sound,
Maybe it was a scared animal?
It wasn't, it was a . . .
  A jumping something!

**Harry Grose (10)**
**Our Lady Of Lourdes RC Primary School, Leigh-On-Sea**

# Seasonal Haikus

*Spring*
Plants want to be free
They want to show their colours
Children are playing.

*Summer*
A baking hot day
A beautiful summer's breeze
Very big heat wave.

*Autumn*
Cool days in autumn
Crispy leaves all on the floor
And a mild, fresh breeze.

*Winter*
Children in the snow
Snowflakes falling from the sky
God makes the snow fall.

**George Mellish  (9)**
**St John's RC Primary School, Rotherhithe**


# Great Holidays

Holidays, holidays are so fun,
Not unless you say it's dumb.
Holidays, holidays can be sunny,
So why not go and buy some honey?
Holidays, holidays, it can be funny
But sometimes it's not so sunny.

Holidays, holidays are so hot,
So why not plant flowers in an old flower pot?
Holidays, holidays, bring out some pies,
But there's so many flies.
Holidays, holidays, you may go to the beach,
Then lay back and have a peach.

**Celine Howe  (8)**
**St John's RC Primary School, Rotherhithe**

# Seasonal Haikus

*Spring*
Children are playing
In the hot, warm air of spring
Plants want to be free.

*Summer*
Hot air of summer
World grows flowers all around
It is so lovely.

*Autumn*
Leaves fall off the trees
Flowers start to fade away
Autumn showers fall.

*Winter*
Cold winds of winter
Snowflakes falling from the sky
God makes the snow fall.

**Robert Lavelle  (9)**
**St John's RC Primary School, Rotherhithe**

# Fun Holidays

I lolidayc, holidays can be fun,
Not unless they catch your tongue.
Holidays, holidays are so sunny,
So go and find me some honey.
Holidays, holidays are so sunny
But sometimes it's not as funny.
Holidays, holidays are so funny
But most of the time it is sunny.

Holidays, holidays are so sunny,
All the best for being funny.
Holidays, holidays are made for fun,
So that we can catch the sun.
Holidays, holidays are really fun
And you get to lay in the sun.

**Shea Mitchell  (8)**
**St John's RC Primary School, Rotherhithe**

# Seasonal Haikus

*Spring*
Spring is Easter's month
The month we get Easter eggs
And the flowers grow.

*Summer*
In the summer park
Watching the flowers blossom
Growing every day.

*Autumn*
Autumn is the month
When leaves crinkle and get cold
And when trees go bare.

*Winter*
A cold, winter breeze
Swirling round and through the air
Making people shiver.

**Conor Hynes (9)**
**St John's RC Primary School, Rotherhithe**


# Holidays

Holidays are fun.
I went to Spain.
I went to the funfair to have some fun.
In the night it was cold.
In Spain it was hot.
I got up and went swimming to have fun.
The pool was cold and wavy.
Then in the night there was a disco.

**Grace Day (8)**
**St John's RC Primary School, Rotherhithe**

# Seasonal Haikus

*Spring*
Ah, so warm spring breeze
Flowers are blossoming now
Lovely warm weather.

*Summer*
A great summer day
Oh, what a lovely breeze
We go on the beach.

*Autumn*
Oh, the nice red leaves
Ah, we're jumping in leaf piles
Oh, nice autumn breeze.

*Winter*
Ah, so fun winter
Oh, the breeze is bitter cold
Snowball fights are great.

**Alan Phee  (8)**
**St John's RC Primary School, Rotherhithe**


# At The Ghost House

At the ghost house
Two people haunted it
One man, one woman
Screams shout every night
Next door wonder
What to do
One night three children
Wander up to the door
On Hallowe'en night
One boo
Three children ran away
Next door wondered
What to do.

**Shannon Donovan  (8)**
**St John's RC Primary School, Rotherhithe**

# Swimming

The swimming pool is hot and cold,
Your fingers and toes start to bold.
Swimming is fun,
Especially when you're swimming in the sun.
Sometimes the water is hot,
Sometimes not.
Most people like breaststroke,
A few like backstroke.

Sometimes we use floats,
People are even as fast as banana boats.
The swimming teacher starts to yell,
As loud as the school bell.
The swimming teacher is very angry
And I am feeling very hungry.
As the teacher has a shout,
We all get out.

**Jessie Agnew (8)**
**St John's RC Primary School, Rotherhithe**

# Holidays

Holidays are fun
I went to Spain
I went to the funfair to have some fun.
It was hot and sunny.
In the night I was dreadful.
When I got up I went to breakfast.
Then I went swimming.
It was cold and wavy.
In the night I went to a disco.
It was lovely and nice.
I danced all night.
Then I went home to bed.

**Nicole White (8)**
**St John's RC Primary School, Rotherhithe**

# Seasonal Poems

*Spring*
The nice breeze in spring
Tall flowers rise up high in the sky
The nice breeze in the grass.

*Summer*
The burning sky waits
Nice land burns under power
The smoky sky waits.

*Autumn*
In autumn leaves fall
The trees are crooked on land
In the wind it's cold.

*Winter*
The winter so cold
So the tornado blows bad
Face cracks in the wind.

**Daniel Odeyale  (9)**
**St John's RC Primary School, Rotherhithe**

# Seasonal Poems

*Spring*
Flowers grow in the air
Little raindrops fall from the sky
Nice breeze in the air.

*Summer*
The hot sun, no wind
Lions roar in the summer
The hot sun burning.

*Autumn*
Leaves falling off trees
Branches crunchy and crispy
Cold wind is blowing.

*Winter*
The cold breeze
Cold snowflakes coming from the sky
Squirrels slipping on ice.

**Barney Williams  (9)**
**St John's RC Primary School, Rotherhithe**

# Seasonal Haikus

*Spring*
Green grass growing tall
Butterflies fly very high
The birds sing and play.

*Summer*
Hot air and warm breeze
Bright blue sky with no such clouds
Big, bright, shining sun.

*Autumn*
Children come out now
Trees are leafless and leaves fall
Leaves are everywhere.

*Winter*
Hard, slippery ice
And cold air and icy breeze
Snowy every day.

**Paula Torren  (9)**
**St John's RC Primary School, Rotherhithe**

## Seasonal Poems

*Spring*
Spring flowers grow and grow
In the park birds sing and sing
And go to the beach.

*Summer*
In the summer park
The summer flowers bloom
With hot weather.

*Autumn*
The autumn weather
Lovely day
For outside.

*Winter*
Winter, cool and cool
It's cool with lots of snow
Winter, cold as ice.

**Ryan Clark  (9)**
**St John's RC Primary School, Rotherhithe**

# Seasonal Poems

*Spring*
Trees, leaves fallen again
The sky flies on the air
And everywhere around houses and buildings.

*Summer*
Leaves grow on trees everywhere
We can eat ice cream anytime
We can't stop drinking.

*Autumn*
Roasted leaves and crunchy leaves
That fall off trees, falling down to the ground
Falling and falling.

*Winter*
We can skate on ice
And throw snowballs at each other
And get freezing cold.

**Oliver Mamendyi (8)**
**St John's RC Primary School, Rotherhithe**

# Seasonal Poems

*Winter*
People like the snow
And people can throw snowballs
And then it turns to ice.

*Summer*
In the summer It's hot
And you could catch a burn
It is very hot.

*Autumn*
Crackly leaves come down
All leaves coming down from the tree
It looks quite pretty.

*Spring*
All of the leaves come
Then it looks much better
People can see spring.

**Conor Crawley  (9)**
**St John's RC Primary School, Rotherhithe**

# Seasonal Haikus

*Spring*
In spring flowers bloom
The trees sway with blossoms on
No clouds in the sky.

*Summer*
The hot summer days
The lovely beach waits for us
The sun is burning.

*Autumn*
In autumn red leaves
Fall with the brisk winds that blow
No clouds in the sky.

*Winter*
The icy snowflakes
That drip on your frozen tongue
You will love winter.

**Dominique Vasquez  (9)**
**St John's RC Primary School, Rotherhithe**

# Seasonal Haikus

*Spring*
The flowers are cold
The sun is getting brighter
In the shiny air.

*Summer*
A hot and dry time
Very warm in Africa
The flowers are nice.

*Autumn*
It is turning cold
The flowers are dying quick
The air is so cold.

*Winter*
The flowers have died
The leaves are changing colours
In the gloomy air.

**Nufi Biriyok  (9)**
**St John's RC Primary School, Rotherhithe**